絵物語

# ドミナの園

春川ナミオ

ドミニク・ウルフ 英訳

58才にしては老けたハゲの小男、秋山春男は見掛けに反し、業界注目の社長である。大手化粧品会社の商品開発部門を研究一筋に歩み、若くして部長に抜擢されたやり手だったが女性には無縁で、40才の時、独身の身軽さから独立起業。自らの化粧品会社を興し、死にもの狂いで働いた結果、10年後には社員150人を擁する注目企業の社長となった。
広告が当たって、若い女性の間で話題となり、新たなテレビCMの撮影をすることになった。その現場で、起用したモデルの大原加奈に出会った春男は、豊かな肉体から発せられる圧倒的な美に打ち震え、ただただ彼女の手を握りしめた。
やがてテレビからは、全国に向けて加奈のメッセージが流れはじめた。
「貴女も美人堂の化粧品で美しく輝いて、男を手玉にとってみませんか」

A short, bald man—old for his 58 years—Akiyama Haruo was, despite his displeasing looks, a corporate leader who commanded the attention of his industry. First working in the research and development division of a major cosmetics manufacturer, Haruo soon found himself promoted to a top managerial position. Unburdened by a woman who might depend on him, he took risks that only bachelorhood could allow, and by 40, he had begun his own company. Working like a dog paid off for Haruo. Within a decade, this little man had built up a major cosmetics line, was running an operation with more than 150 employees, and had become president of Lady Luster, one of the country's leading cosmetic firms.

The advertising was effective too. Word spread fast among the young women. And, it became time to shoot a new television commercial. It was there, on the shoot, that Haruo met Ohara Kana, the company model. Overwhelmed by the beauty emanating from her voluptuous body, all that little Haruo could do was to earnestly grasp Kana's hand.

Before long, Kana's message was being broadcast across the country: "Glisten with Lady Luster! And wrap a man around your finger!"

撮影以来、加奈を思い、悶々とする春男。「あのまばゆい肢体に屈服しない男はいまい。是が非でもこの思いを伝えねば」と、年甲斐もなく自制心を失い、加奈に連絡をとると、ホテルのスイートルームを予約した。
当日、部屋で待ちわびる春男の元に、ノックの音に続いて、笑顔の加奈が現れた。
「社長さん、こんにちは。お元気でしたか」
正面に迫る豊かなバストに、春男は「お忙しいところを申し訳ありません……加奈さん、お願いがあります」と言い終らぬうちに、思わず加奈にしがみついていた。加奈は素早く春男の頭を腕で締めあげ胸に押し付けた。
「す、すみません。お許し下さい。苦しい、許してください」
春男を離し、加奈が答えた。
「もう、びっくりしたわ。どういうわけか話してください」

After the shoot, Haruo tormented himself with thoughts of Kana. He knew any man would surrender himself to that glistening body. And he knew, too, that even if he were wrong, he still just had to get to know her better. Forgetting his age and his self-control too, Haruo contacted Kana. His next move was to get a hotel suite.
On the appointed day, as Haruo sat in the room he'd reserved, the sound of knocking was followed by Kana's smiling face. "Mr. President, hello! Have you been well?" And to the voluptuous bust that was closing in, Haruo announced, "Kana-san, I'm sorry to bother you when you are so busy, but I have to ask you something." Before he had even finished these words, he had thrown himself against Kana. Not missing a beat, Kana nimbly caught Haruo's head with her two hands and pressed it firmly to her breast.
"I'm so... sorry. Please forgive me. Oh... Owww. That hurts. Please forgive me."
Setting Haruo free, Kana replied, "What's come over you? Whatever it is, you had better explain yourself."

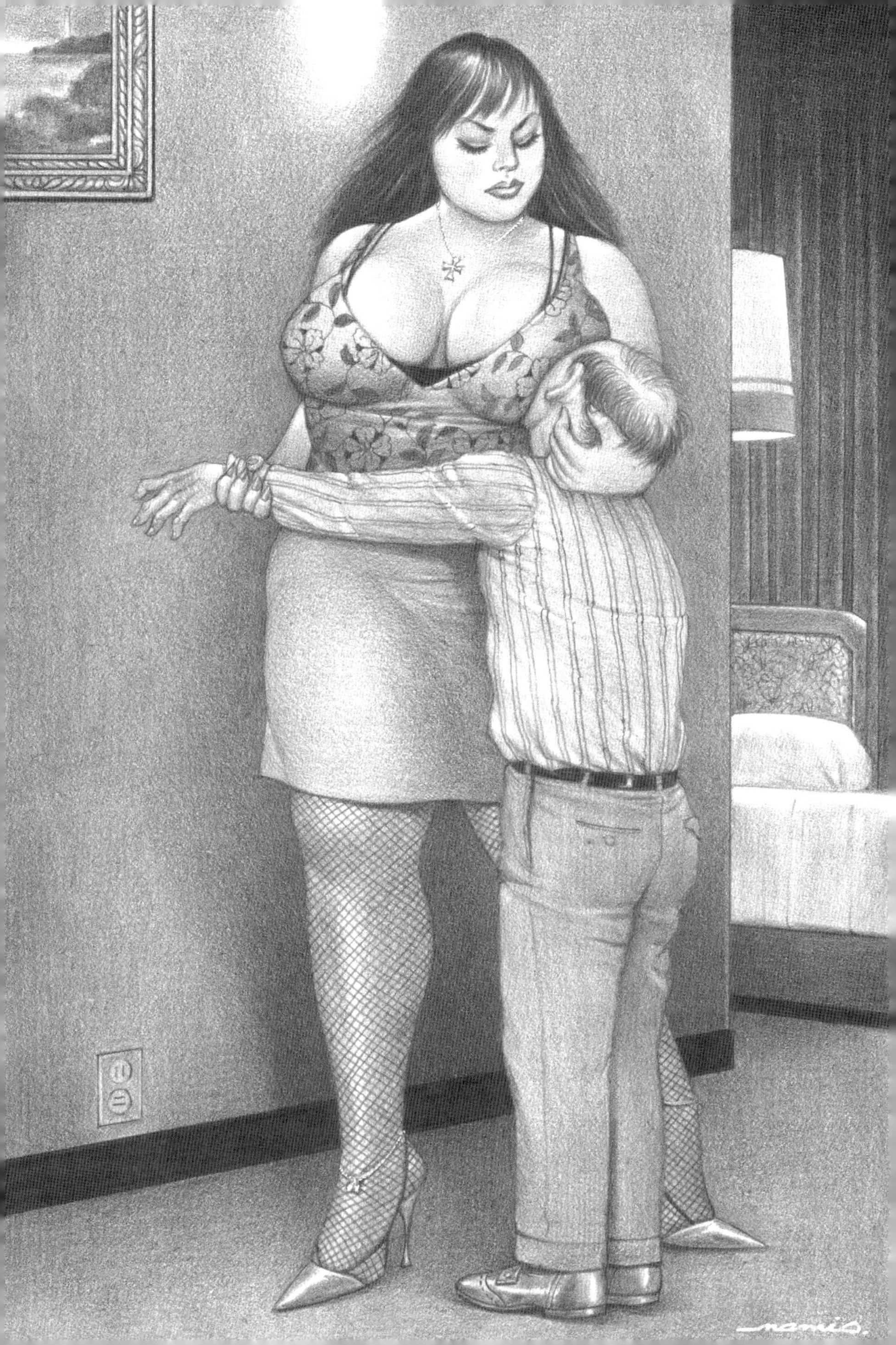
namio.

足下に正座する春男に、加奈はソファを勧めたが、春男は固辞した。
「ソファだなんて、とんでもない。これが私の真の姿なのです」
目に涙をためて加奈を見上げ、春男は、自分のM的性格について告白した。
「それで、どうして欲しいの?」
「私を加奈さんの奴隷にして下さい。加奈さんの巨大なお尻に敷かれたいのです」
「巨大だなんて、失礼ね。フフフ……。でも、本当に大きいわよ」
「最高です。どうか忠実なる僕(しもべ)として私をお使いください。いかなる条件もお受けいたします」
「いいわ、私の奴隷になりたいのね」
加奈はパンティを脱ぎ捨てると、春男の目の前にヒップを突き出した。そして、春男は夢中で巨大な谷間に顔を埋めた。
「フフ……。可愛いわ。私のお尻に顔を埋めて泣いているなんて。ほら、もっとお泣き!!」

Kana suggested to Haruo, kneeling as he was by her feet, that he take the sofa. But Haruo flatly refused. "Me, on the sofa?! How could I when this is my true position?" With tears brimming in his eyes, Haruo looked up towards Kana and confessed his masochistic nature.
"I don't understand what you're asking."
"Please make me your slave, Miss Kana. I want you to sit on me with your tremendous *oshiri*."
"Tremendous... why, there's no reason to be rude... But, yes, my *oshiri* certainly is large."
"It's magnificent. Please use me as your faithful manservant. I'll agree to any conditions you name."
"So, you want to be my slave. That's fine with me."
Removing her panties and tossing them aside, Kana thrust her hips right into Haruo's line of sight. And, in a dream come true, the little man buried his face into the magnificent valley between them.
"Ho! Ho! Ho! What a charming sight you are. Crying as your face buries itself in my *oshiri*... Well, then, cry yourself some more tears!"

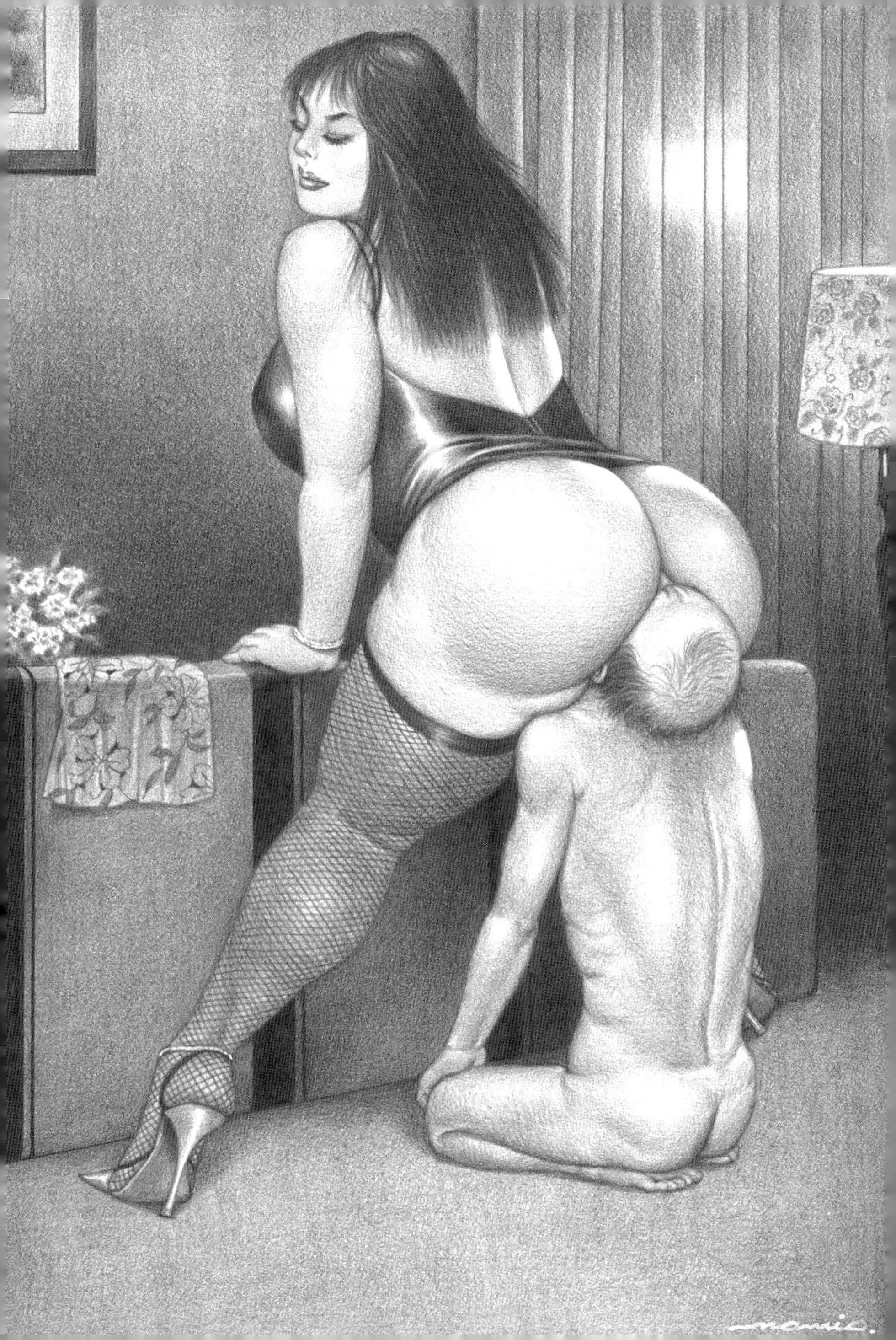

加奈は、自分のお尻に顔を埋めて涙する小男に優越感を覚えると、もっといじめてやりたくなり、春男にソファに仰向けに寝るように命じた。
春男があわてて、ひじかけに頭を置き、ソファに横になると、顔面を巨大なヒップが覆った。
「私のお尻がどれだけ重いかわからせてあげるわ。本気で体重をかけたら顔がつぶれるかもよ。さあ、何か言ってごらん」
「シ、シアワセです。く、くるしい」
煙草を燻らしながら、加奈は体重をかける。
「お尻の間に顔がめりこんでゆくわ。こんな勝ち誇った気持ちははじめて。ああ、もがいている。ほら、もっと苦しめ、ほら!」
やがて苦しみもがいていた春男は動かなくなった。

Slowly entranced by a feeling of superiority over this puny, little man with his teary face planted in her ass, Kana ordered Haruo to lie on his back on the sofa. Haruo wasted no time in placing his head on the armrest and his body on the sofa. In an instant, he was covered by those tremendous hips.
"I'm going to let you see how heavy my *oshiri* is. Who knows? If really I put my full weight on it, your face will be crushed. Go on, now! Say something!"
"Ww... wha... what bliss! I... I... it hurts."
Puffing at her cigarette, Kana lowered herself further upon him.
"Your face is lodged right in my *oshiri*. I don't think I've ever felt so victorious. You're struggling now. Come on, now, suffer it some more."
Eventually Haruo, who had first been writhing in pain, ceased to move.

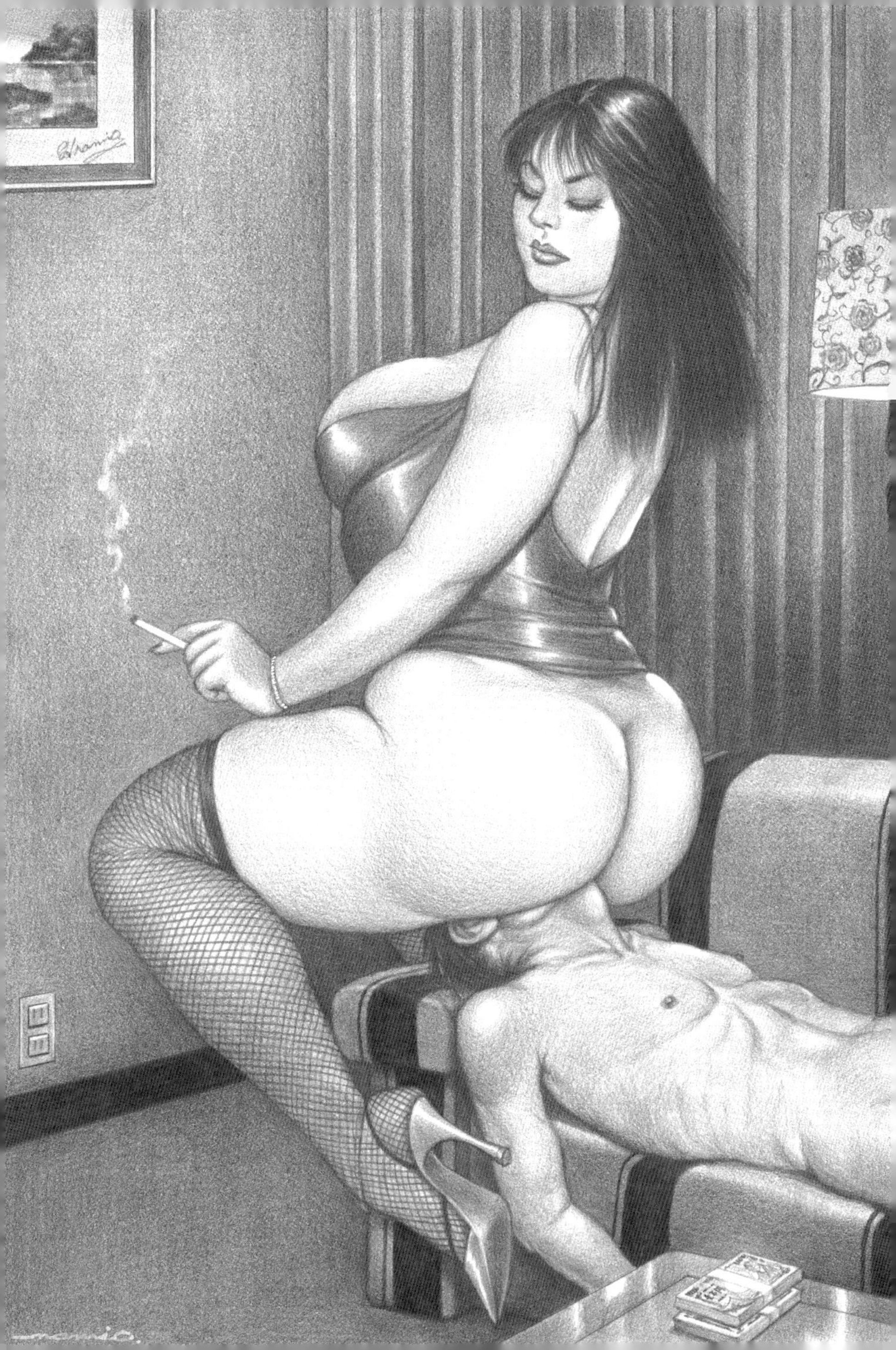

失神した春男の頬に、加奈の平手打ちが飛ぶと、気づいた春男の目から一すじの涙がこぼれた。
満足そうに便器に腰を下ろした加奈がやがて叫んだ。
「あら、紙がないわ！　困ったわね!」
春男は便器の前で平伏し「私の舌をお使いください」と答えた。
「わかったわ。舌できれいにしてちょうだい。お尻の穴よ。そう、もっと奥まで入れるのよ。さあ、お前はどんな気持ち？」
「最高です。死んでも構いません。ありがとうございます。実はトイレットペーパーは私が隠しました。どうかお許しください」
「合格！　お前を奴隷にしてやるわ。条件は絶対服従。命令に反したら殺す。それから、私をお前の会社で雇い、二人だけのときは加奈様とお呼び。私はお前を春と呼ぶわ。毎月給料とは別に100万を小遣いとしてよこすこと。このテーブルの上の200万は貰っておくわ。分かったわね。分かったら口をお開け！　いくわよ!」

Kana slapped her hand against the unconscious Haruo's cheek. When coming to, he shed a single tear. At first pleased to settle her bottom onto the toilet seat, Kana finally raised her voice. "There's no paper here. What am I going to do?"
Prostrate in front of the bowl, Haruo meekly suggested, "Please use my tongue."
"You hopeless pervert! Go ahead, then! Use your tongue to clean it . Clean the hole to my *oshiri*. Yes, go deeper. How do you feel now?"
"I'm in heaven. I could die now. Thank you very much. Actually, I hid the toilet paper. Will you please forgive me for that?"
"You're lucky. I'll be kind enough to make you my slave. But I require complete submission. If you disobey me, you're dead."
"You're going to make me an employee at your company. And you're to call me Mistress Kana, when it's just the two of us. I will call you Haru. In addition to my regular salary, you'll provide me with a million yen allowance per month. And, yes, I'll be taking the two million out there on the table. You understand? If you understand, you should open your mouth. Alright, here goes…"

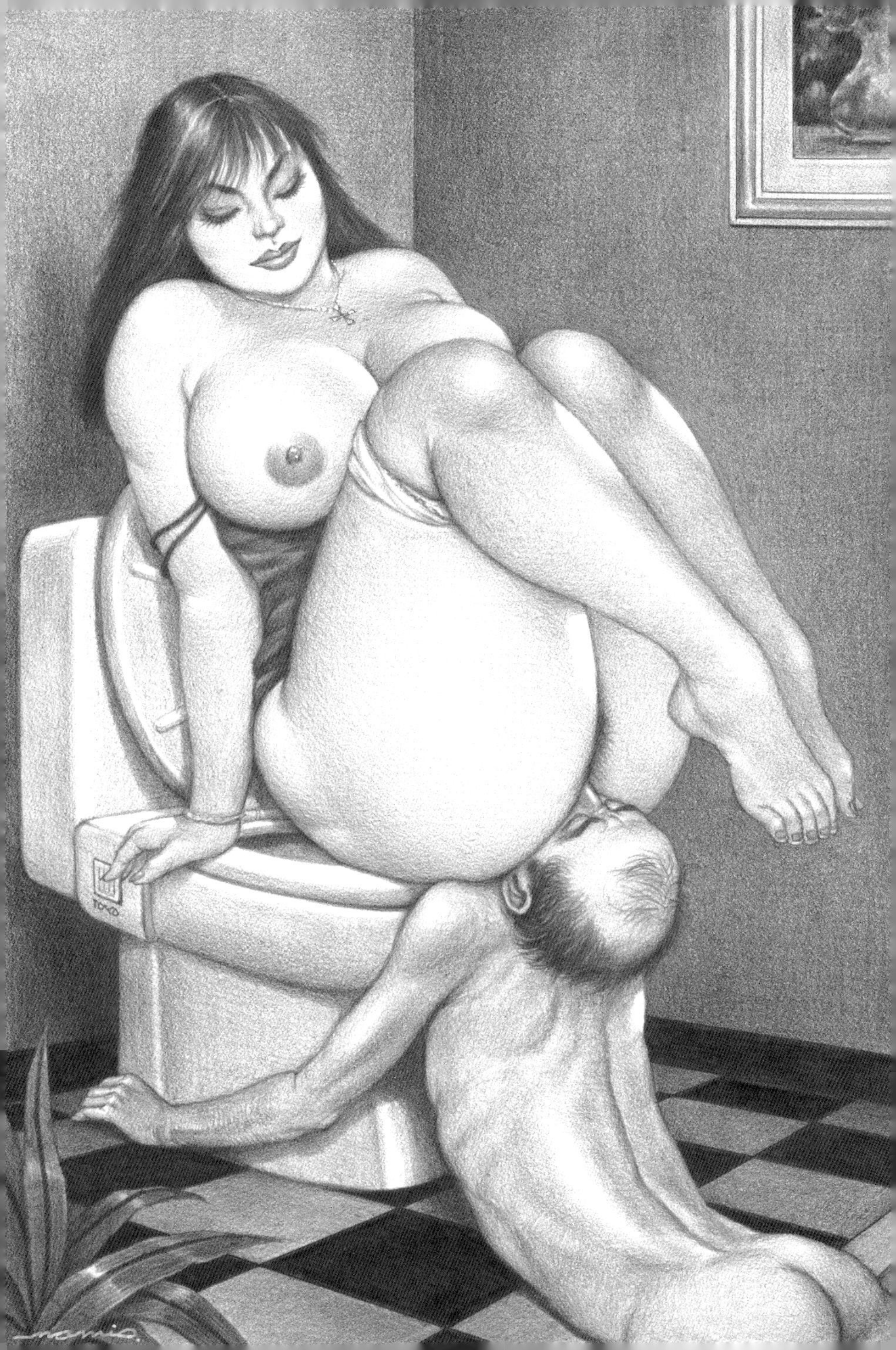

1週間後、加奈は美人堂に出社した。ダブルの背広を着て、社長然とした春男が自分の忠実な奴隷かと思うと、新たな野心が芽生えていた。
春男は加奈を紹介するために大会議室に全社員を集めた。190cm超の加奈の美貌を目の当たりに一同は驚きを隠せない。
「本日付けで我が社にお迎えすることになった大原加奈さんです。バレーボールの全日本代表として活躍された後、モデルになり多くの女性の支持を集めていることは、ご存知と思います。コマーシャルが縁で、当社の総務部秘書課長として働いていただくことになりました」
いきなり課長に抜擢、しかも豊満なバストとヒップを揺らして目の前を歩く加奈に男性社員は戸惑った。誘惑に負けてお尻に触れてしまった営業部の木村主任を、加奈は退社時間を見計らい呼びつけた。
「貴方は失礼な男ね。そんなに私のお尻が好きなら、どんなものなのか教えてあげる」
木村を力で捩じ伏せるや、その顔の上に巨大なヒップを下ろした。

A week later, Kana appeared for work at Lady Luster. Knowing that Haruo, always very presidential in his double-breasted suit, was in fact her faithful slave, Kana felt a newfound ambition well up within her.
Haruo called for a company-wide meeting in order to introduce Kana to all his employees. Her beautiful stature —she was a tall woman at over 190 cm— took the assembled audience by surprise.
"I am delighted to welcome to Lady Luster today Ohara Kana. I think you are all familiar with Ms. Ohara's career playing for the All-Japan Volleyball Team and her work in modeling, where she has won the support of many of Japan's women. Ms. Ohara will be joining us as Chief of Secretarial Staff in our General Affairs Division."
The company's male employees were intrigued not only by Kana's sudden promotion to Secretarial Chief but also at her voluptuous bust and hips, shimmying as she walked before them.
Mr. Kimura, the head of the Sales Division, couldn't control himself, and patted her *oshiri*. But Kana cornered him at the end of the day.
"You're a dirty little man, Kimura. If you're so curious about my *oshiri*, I'll show you what it's really like."
She pinned him down and lowered those tremendous hips onto his face. [190 cm = 6'3"]

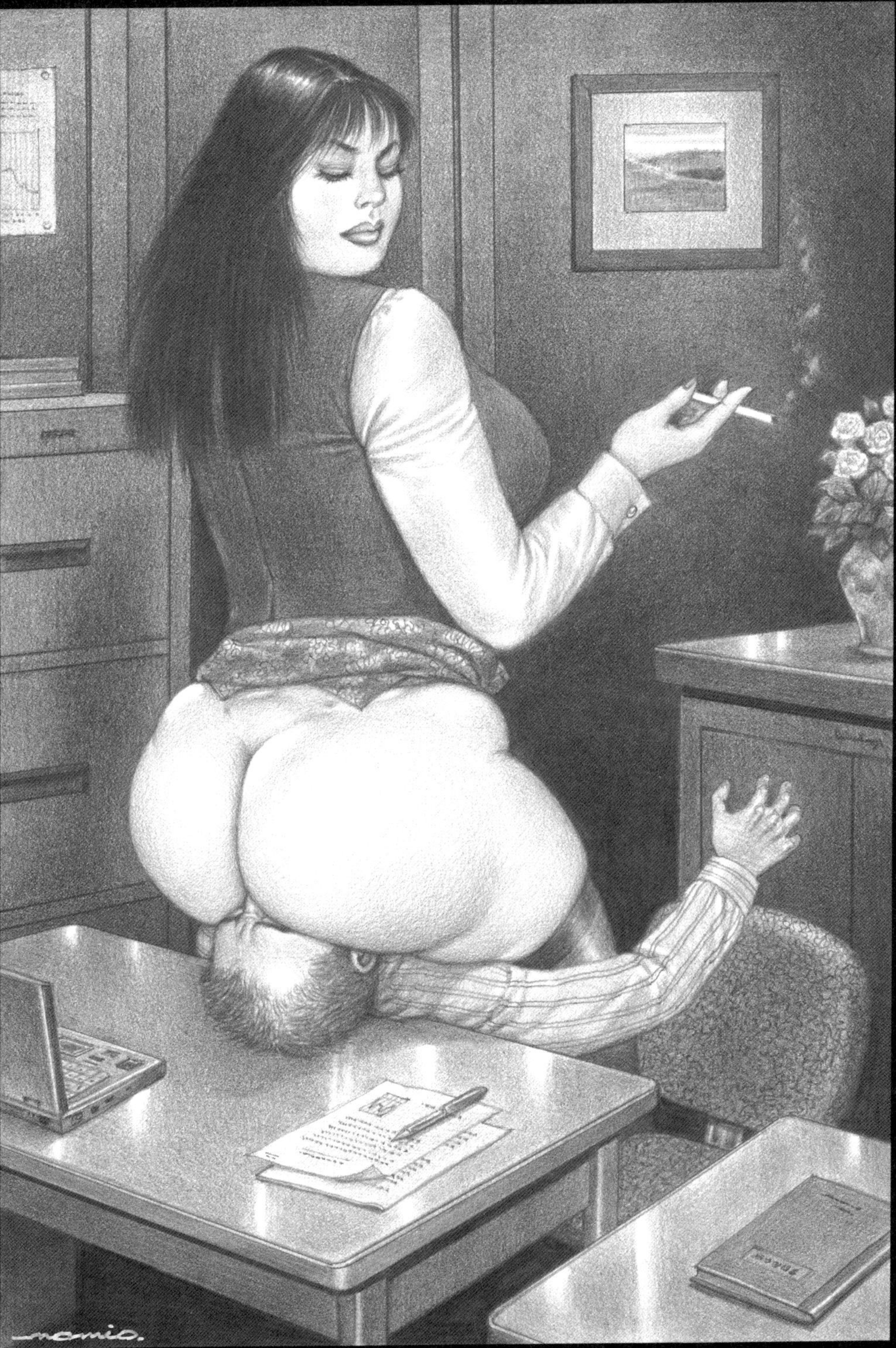
namio.

男性社員たちは仕事中も加奈のお尻を目で追っている。そのくせ、女性社員をお茶くみに甘んじさせる時代錯誤をなんとかせねばならない。
そこで、女性とお尻の偉大さをもっと知らしめてやろうと加奈は超ミニスカートをはき、社内を闊歩した。男性社員たちはますます仕事どころではない。経理の山本課長も、たまらずにお尻に手を伸ばしてきた。加奈は退社しようとする山本を呼び止めた。
「そんなにお尻が好きなら、よく見るがいい」
加奈は山本の両手を事務椅子の脚に縛りつけると、その顔にお尻が密着するよう腰をおろし、コーヒーを味わった。
「ほら、お前の好きなお尻よ」
加奈は顔を圧迫する。
「もっと苦しめてあげるわ。舌を伸ばして舐めてごらん。届かないわね。いいわ、口をお開け!!　オナラをあげるわ、ホホホホ…」

Even while they were at work, the male employees would shadow Kana's *oshiri* with their eyes. This made Kana all the more determined to reform the outdated custom whereby women staff made tea for the men.
The male employees were ignorant of the power of a woman—and ignorant too of the power in an *oshiri*. So, Kana took to wearing mini-skirts and strutting about the office. The men had even more trouble getting their work done. Accounting Manager Mr. Yamamoto couldn't stop himself reaching for a feel. Kana stopped him as he made his way out of the office one day.
"If you like *oshiri* so very much, then you'd better inspect one." She tied Yamamoto's arms to the leg of an office chair. Then as she lowered her waist so that her *oshiri* would touch his face, she took a sip of coffee.
"See, here is the *oshiri* you like so much." Kana pressed herself against his face. "I'll make you suffer more. Reach out your tongue and take a lick. Oh, you're not reaching. Alright, now, open your mouth. I'm going to pass some gas. Ha! Ha! Ha!"

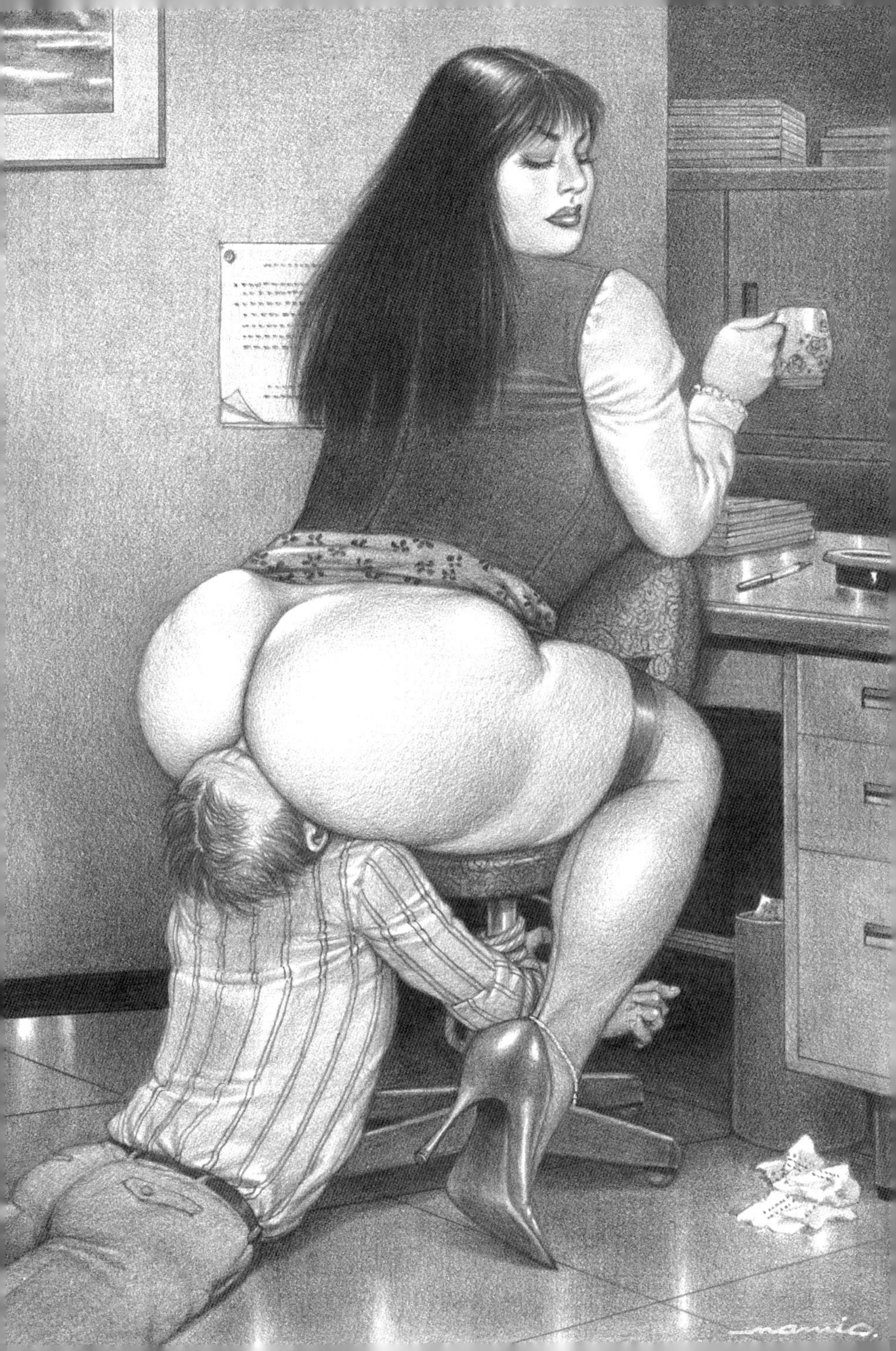

加奈が入社して1ヶ月が過ぎた頃、すでに20人の男性社員が、終業後の加奈の懲戒を密かに受けた。あるとき同じ課の松本が残るように命じられた。
「私のロッカーを開けてパンティの匂いを嗅いでいたわね」
「ごめんなさい。許してください」
「私の命令に従うなら許してあげてもいいわ」
「何でも言うことをききます」
加奈は机の上に座ると、パンティをとり、松本の目の前で脚を開いた。
「さあ、いらっしゃい。お舐め、パンティじゃなく本物よ」
松本はおずおず加奈のクレバスに顔を近づけると、生え繁った剛毛を掻き分け、必死で舌を伸ばした。
「舌が届いたわ、さあ、気持ちよくさせてごらん。もっとお舐め。あ～、いいわ」
加奈の逞しい太腿が締まると、強烈な肉圧に松本は力尽きた。

016

Within a month of Kana's joining the firm, twenty of the male employees had received Kana's private discipline. One day, Matsumoto, who worked in the same section, was ordered to stay behind.
"You opened my locker and sniffed my panties, didn't you, Matsumoto?"
"I'm very sorry. Please forgive me."
"I'll consider forgiving you if you follow my orders."
"Ms. Ohara, I'll do whatever you say."
Sitting on the desk, Kana removed her panties and opened her legs wide for Matsumoto to see.
"Come on now, boy. Come take a lick. Not my panties… the real thing."
Matsumoto timidly approached Kana's crevice, and as he pushed his way through the thick of her bush, he stuck out a desperate tongue.
"I can feel your tongue. Now, try to make me feel good. Lick more. Ahh… now that's good."
When Kana shut her brawny thighs, Matsumoto became immobilized by her indomitable body.

室蘭

入社2ヶ月で、加奈はすべての男性社員をお尻で征服した。
加奈に従順な男性社員と、ますます美しくなる加奈を見て、女子社員たちは加奈に憧れ、敬い、職場の空気は劇的に変わった。加奈は範を示すように女子社員たちの前で男たちをお尻の下に敷き、いたぶった。
「前田君、今、何時だと思っているの。今日も遅刻だわね」
加奈の強烈な平手が前田の頬に飛んだ。
「申し訳ありません。お許しください」
「許さないわ、君は反省をしてない。分からせてあげるから、服を脱いで手を後ろに回しなさい」
加奈は前田を後ろ手に縛りあげると仰向けに頭を椅子の上に乗せ、パンティを下げると怯える前田に容赦なく巨大なお尻を見舞った。
「今日は一日このままで仕事よ。泣いても許さないわ。お尻の重さを感じながら責任の重さを知るといい。女子社員たちを前に、私のお尻の下で失神するのも乙なものよ、ホホホホ……」

Within two months, Kana had conquered each and every Lady Luster male employee with her *oshiri*. Both the male employees, obedient as they were to Kana, and the female employees, witnesses to Kana's beauty which was growing by the day, fell passionately for her, and the mood of the office transformed. Providing a primer for the other female employees, Kana frequently positioned the men under her bottom and tormented them

"Maeda, do you know what time it is? You're late again today."

Kana's powerful palm struck Maeda's cheek. "I am truly very sorry. Please forgive me."

"I certainly will not, as you show no remorse."

Kana tied Maeda's arms behind his back and placed his head, facing upwards, upon a chair. Lowering her panties, she began to slap the frightened Maeda with her tremendous bottom.

"You'll be working all day like this. Cry all you like, I won't change my mind. When you feel the weight of this *oshiri*, it should remind you of the burden of your responsibilities. Under the weight of my *oshiri*, you can go ahead and faint right in front of all the women employees here."

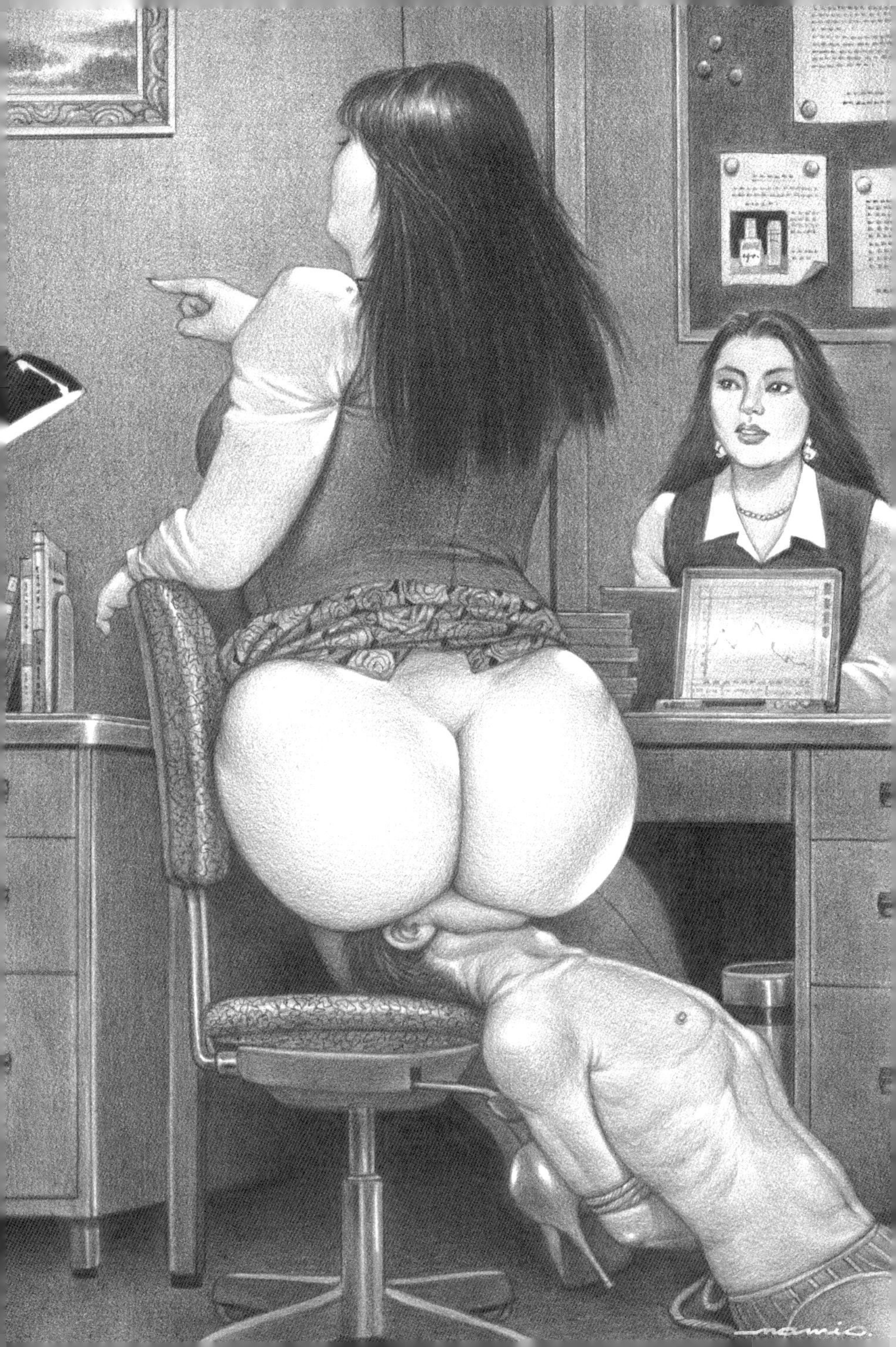

入社1年後、大原加奈は取締役総務部長に昇格。もう誰も加奈に逆らう者はいない。思い描いた通りである。加奈が営業部の木村を社長室に呼びつけた。
「大原部長、な、何でしょうか」
「君は営業のくせに言葉の使い方も知らないようね。教育する必要があるわ。服を脱いで、こっちに来なさい。さ、早く!!」
加奈は、パンツ1枚になった木村を縛ると、春男の前に仁王立ちになり、巨尻を出し、命じた。
「木村、早く、お尻に顔をお付け。ほらっ、もっとしっかり顔を入れるのよ」
巨大な谷間で苦しむ木村。
「ホホホ、社長の前でいい格好ね。さあ舌を伸ばしてごらん、届かないわね」
加奈は両手でお尻を開いてやる。
「ようやく穴に届いたわね。ほら、お舐め!! しっかり。そうよ、いいわよ」
羨ましそうに眺める春男に加奈は微笑みながら片目をつぶってみせた。

Just a short year after she'd joined Lady Luster, Ohara Kana was promoted to an executive position. Not a soul in the company dared oppose Kana, and things always happened just as she wanted them. Kana called Mr. Kimura from Sales over to the President's office.
"Ms. Ohara, wh... what might be the problem?"
"You're in Sales, and you don't even know how to address someone politely? I'll teach you. Get your clothes off and get over here. Hurry up!"
Having tied up Kimura, now reduced to his underpants, Kana turned to Haruo. Towering in front of Haruo, she stuck out her massive buttocks and ordered Kimura below:
"Hurry up and put your face in my *oshiri*. Come on now, push it deeper." Kimura suffered in the expansive valley. "Just look at yourself, right in front of the President."
"Now stick out your tongue. You're not reaching far enough." Kana spread open her bottom with her hands. "Finally, you've reached the hole. Go on now, boy, and lick. Very good." Towards Haruo, who was looking on jealously, Kana offered a faint smile and a wink.

社長

加奈は春男をソファに座らせると、その膝の上に乗り、両足を開き、木村に命じた。
「木村、こっちへ来て気持ちよくさせてごらん。君の舌は気持ちいいわ、なかなか上手よ」
木村は加奈の足の間で腹這いになると、クレバスに顔を埋めた。
加奈は気持ちよさそうに、タバコをふかし目を細める。さらに、両脚を開くと、木村は繁みに埋もれ、必死で舌を動かした。
「いいわよ。君の舌は最高よ、もっと。そう、そこ。ほら、もっとお吸い!!」
木村は舌を動かし、吸い続けた。
「いい気持ち。教えてあげるわ。君は交際費を使い過ぎなのよ。どう？　文句があるなら、言ってごらん。あら、言えないのね。ホホホホ、舌の動きが悪いわよ、しっかりお舐め、ああ、いいわ」

Kana made Haruo sit on the sofa, climbed upon his lap, and spread her legs. She then commanded Kimura, "Get over here and make me feel good. Your tongue has got some talent."
Kimura crawled on his stomach in between Kana's legs and buried his face in the crevasse. Clearly enjoying it, Kana half-closed her eyes in pleasure as she puffed on her cigarette. When she opened her legs, Kimura buried himself in the growth and moved his tongue furiously.
"That's good. Your tongue is excellent. More now, right there. Watch it! Now apply some suction."
Kimura moved his tongue and continued sucking.
"That feels so very good. Let me tell you one thing. Your entertainment expenses have got to be cut back. Aren't I right? If you disagree, now is the time to say it… I didn't think so. Ho! Ho! Ho! Your tongue's not moving right. I want you to lick more thoroughly. Ahh, there you have it."

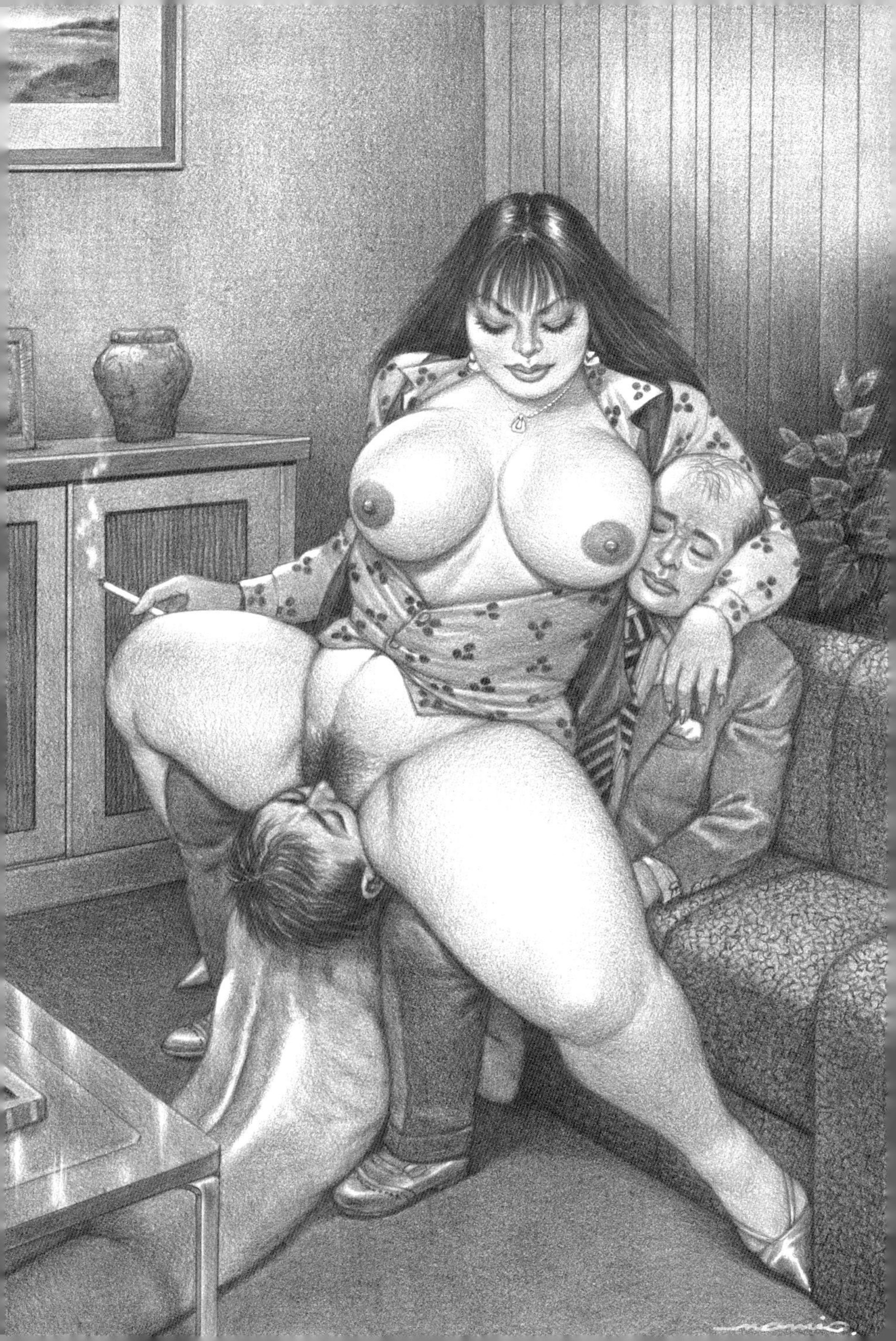

重さに耐えながら、哀しそうな表情を見せる春男に気づいた加奈は膝から降り、抱きしめてやった。春男の顔は120cmを超える巨大バストにすっかり埋もれてしまった。
「あら、バストの間で苦しんでいる社長ったら、とってもかわいいわ。ほら、もっと苦しくするわよ」
加奈は強く春男を抱きしめ、お尻を突き出した。
「木村!!　お尻の穴のまわりをゆっくりお舐め。そう、今度は舌を細く尖らせて奥まで入れてごらん。もっと奥まで!!　届いている、中で動いている、最高に、いい気持ちよ」
夢中で応える木村は、社内で地位を築き辣腕を振るう美しい加奈に奉仕していることに、苦しさ以上に悦びを感じていた。ずっと、このまま奉仕を続けていたい。木村は泣きながら舌を動かしていた。

Noticing Haruo, who had been suffering under her weight with a sad face, Kana got up from his lap and gave him a hug. Haruo's face was completely enfolded in Kana's extra-large bust. "The President looks so adorable buried in my bust. Here, I know you want to suffer it some more." Kana hugged Haruo even harder and stuck out her bottom.
"Kimura! Use your tongue slowly around my *oshiri*'s hole. Yes, but now you're to point your tongue as deeply in as it can go. Deeper! Even deeper! Yes, you're there! Now, move your tongue around inside. That feels just wonderful."
Sure, Kimura was suffering, but Kimura was also lost deep in his fantasy: servicing the beautiful Kana who had established herself so brilliantly in the company and who had shown herself to be such a top performer. If only he could service her forever, Kimura thought, crying as he darted his tongue back and forth.

社長

長時間の奉仕の末、木村が解放された。加奈は分かっていた。自分を差し置いて、木村に奉仕させることに、春男がジェラシーを感じずにいられないことを。加奈は春男に近づくと、平手打ちを食らわし、小柄な春男は、吹っ飛んだ。
「フフ、驚いたでしょ。木村に奉仕させている間のお前ときたら哀しそうだったわ。それが愉しいのよ。お前がジェラシーを感じていることが。さあ、お脱ぎ、早くっ!!」加奈は社長の椅子に座り、巨尻を春男の前に突き出すと「舐めなさい!」と命じた。お尻の割れ目に顔を埋め、夢中で舌を伸ばす春男。
「加奈様、お願いがあります。死ぬほど好きな加奈様のお尻の下で飼い殺されたいのです。加奈様に社長を引き継いでいただき、私は奴隷として生きたいのです」
「わかったわ。お前を飼う代わりに条件を出すわ。私の体から排出するもの以外、決して口にしないこと。わかったわね。ならば口をお開け!! これがお前の食事よ」

After many hours servicing, Kimura was released, but Kana had realized something important in the process: Haruo couldn't help but become jealous at the sight of Kimura, not himself, serving Kana. Returning to Haruo, Kana slapped the puny man off his feet.
"That surprised you, did it??" You looked so miserable the whole time that Kimura was servicing me. But that made me feel so very good. Watching your jealousy was pure delight. Alright now, boy, strip!"
Kana straddled the President's chair, and stuck out her massive buttocks for Haruo to lick. "Lick them!" Haruo pressed his head against the crack of her bottom and, his fantasies realized, stuck out his tongue.
"Mistress Kana, I have a request to make of you. I love Mistress Kana's *oshiri* so much that I could die for it. Useless though I am, I wish Mistress Kana might keep me under that *oshiri* until my dying day. Might Mistress Kana take over from me as President so that I can live my life as Mistress Kana's slave?"
"As you like... but I have conditions if I'm going to be keeping you. You will put nothing into your mouth that has not come out of my body. Do you understand? If so, then open your mouth. Here comes your first meal!"

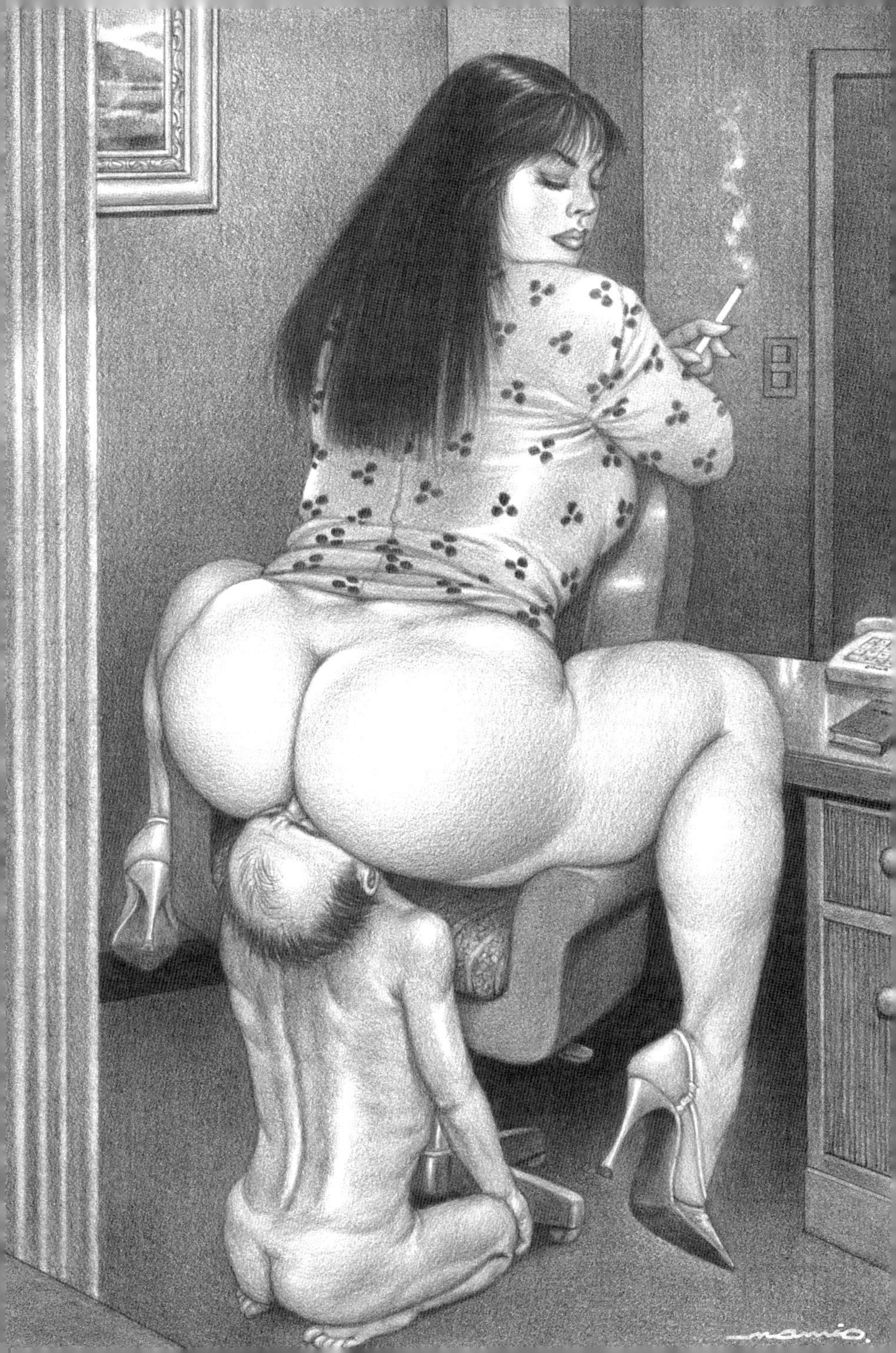

1週間後、美人堂では、体調不良を理由に秋山春男が社長を辞任し、後任に加奈が指名された。加奈は渋谷の高級マンションに移り、そのベッドルームの隣室に鉄製の檻が置かれた。春男の命は完全に加奈に委ねられたのである。1人の男の生死を手中にして加奈は快感に震えた。
新しい湯船にゆったりつかりながら加奈が春男を呼ぶと、裸の春男が飛んで来た。
「仰向けに寝て、頭を椅子の上に乗せてごらん」
横たわる春男の顔面に、神々しい巨尻が覆いかぶさった。
「どう？ お尻の下の奴隷さん。あら、お前の顔が縮んだのかしら、どんどんお尻に埋もれてゆくわ。ホホホ。それとも、また太ったから、私のお尻が大きくなったのかしら。どれだけ重いか教えてあげるわ」
加奈は脚をあげて春男の顔に体重を集中させた。
「お前は今日から、このお尻の下で生きるのよ。いいこと？ あら。動かなくなったわ、また失神してしまったのね」

One week later, citing health reasons, Akiyama Haruo resigned as Lady Luster's President. Kana was named Haruo's successor. Kana moved into a deluxe condominium in the Shibuya District of Tokyo. In the room adjacent to Kana's bedroom sat a metal cage. Haruo had given over his life entirely to Kana. Kana shivered at the pleasures of holding one man's fate in her hands.
Soaking herself in her new tub, Kana called Haruo's name, and the naked man came running.
"Lie on your back, and put your head on the stool."
The sublime and tremendous buttocks extended themselves across the skin of the supine Haruo's face.
"How is it down under my *oshiri*, my little slave? I wonder if your face is shrinking; it's getting buried deeper and deeper into my *oshiri*. Ha! Ha! Ha! Or perhaps, since I've gained some more weight my *oshiri* too has grown. I'll show you just how heavy it's become."
Kana raised her legs and set down her full weight upon Haruo's face. "From today on, you will be living your life under my *oshiri*. Isn't that nice? Oh, you've stopped moving... Have you passed out again?"

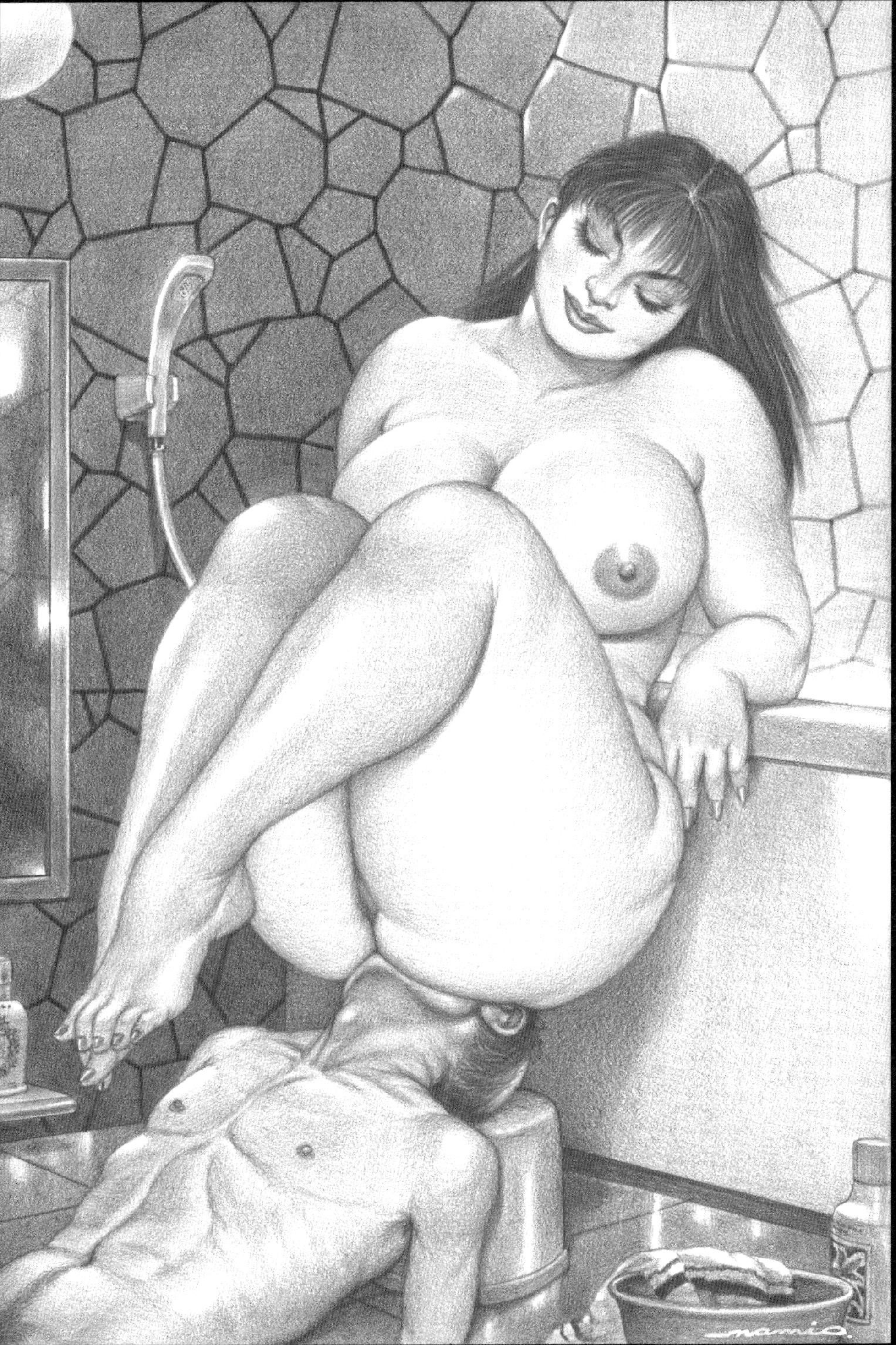

朝起きると、加奈は檻の上にまたがり春男に尿を与える。便意がないときは、夜まで食べ物はない。加奈は春男のため、会社のトイレを極力、利用せずにいた。その加奈の帰りを春男は首を長くして待っている。着替えをすませると、檻に登り、顔の上に跨がる。
「ほほほ、お待ちかねね」
加奈はタバコに火を点けると、春男の舌の感触を愉しんだ。
「しっかりお舐め。そう、おいしそうに音をたてて。いい気持ちよ、ああ、出そう。さあ、吸うのよ、いくわよ」
必死にむしゃぶりつく春男の口にスルっと吸い込まれる。
「しっかりお食べ。まだまだ出るわよ。早く飲まないとこぼれちゃうわよ。ホホホ……。お前が必死な姿を見ると、とてもいい気持ちだわ。ほら、今度は前よ。オシッコも満タンなのよ。いいわね、お前のノドが鳴る音が素敵だわ!」

After waking up in the morning, Kana would stride the cage and feed Haruo her urine. If she had no need to defecate, Haruo would be hungry until the evening. Thinking of Haruo, Kana did her utmost not to use the company's toilets. Haruo would wait at home, his cocked head turned toward the sound of his Mistress' return. After changing out of her office-clothes, Kana would mount the cage and then sit astride Haruo's face.
"You were waiting, I know. Tee, hee, hee."
Kana would light a cigarette and enjoy the sensation of Haruo's tongue.
"Lick it well. Make sure I can hear how delicious it is for you. Oh, that feels good. Oh, it's coming. Suck it out some. I'm going... yes, I'm going."
And, it would slide right into the feverishly sucking Haruo's mouth.
"Eat it all up. There's more coming. If you don't take it down, you'll end up spilling. Ho, ho, ho! When I see you so desperate, I feel so good. But, there's still up front to take care of. My bladder is just full of pee. How marvelous it is to have a man with such throaty skills!"

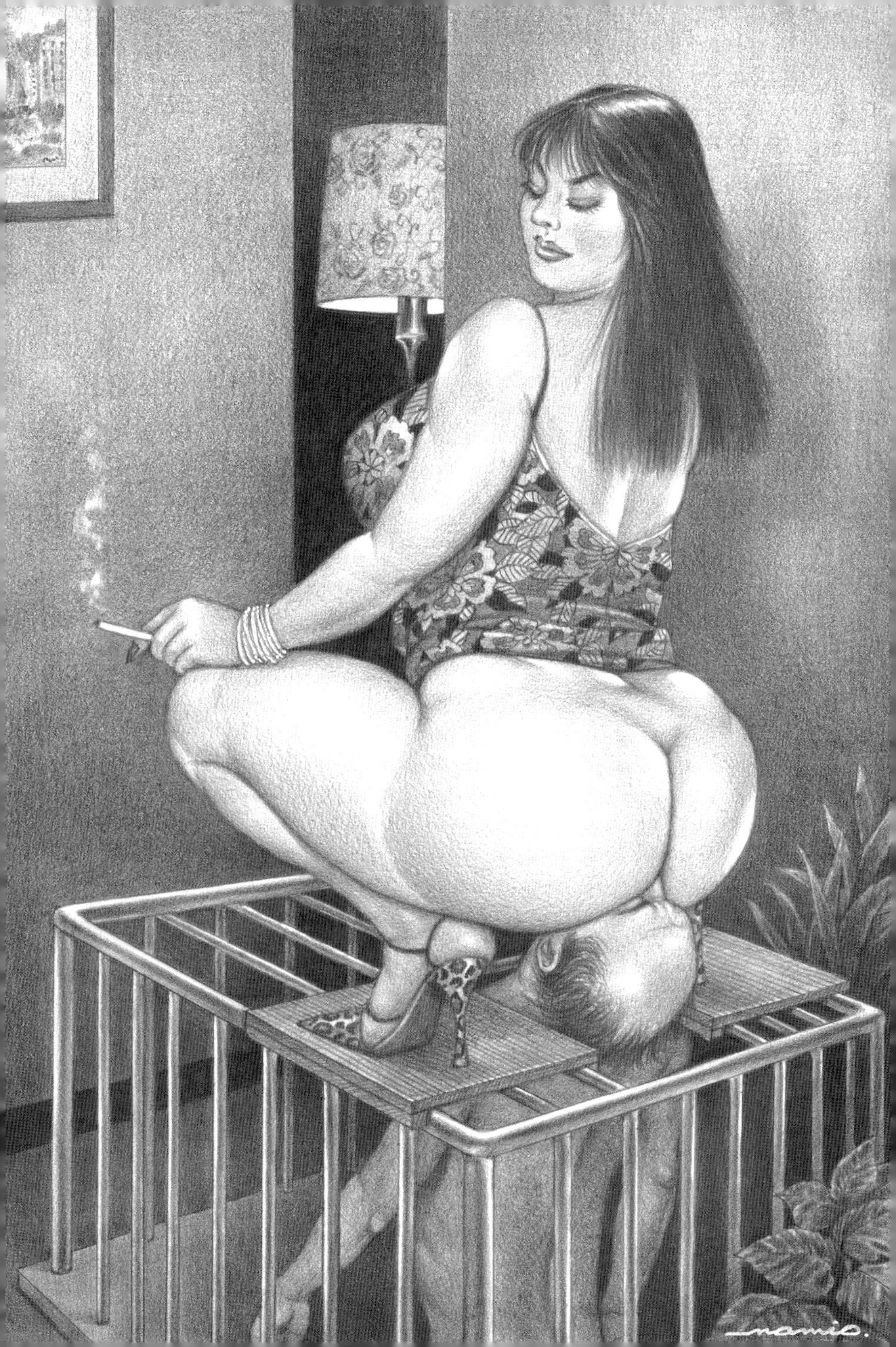
namio.

加奈は部屋にいる時は裸で開放感を味わった。裸で檻の周りを歩いてやると、飢餓感にさらされた春男は、加奈の肉感的なお尻に釘付けになる。一方、加奈も自分の体から出るものすべてを春男に与えてやる。たとえオナラでさえも、思い切り口の中に放った。今まで、こんな優越感を味わったことがあろうか。しかし、このすばらしさを自分だけで愉しんでいいのだろうか。加奈にまたひとつ新たな夢が芽生えていた。

加奈は檻に近づくと、春男の首輪のひもを引き寄せ話しかける。

「さあ、するわよ。いっぱい溜まっているのよ。ほら、お飲み。いい感じで飲んでいるわね。でも、さすがに、この頃、痩せてきたようね。どうなの？　このままでは死んでしまうわよ」

「私は奴隷として生き、今、最高に幸せです。加奈様の専用便器として死ねれば本望でございます」

「ほら、お尻の穴に口をお付け。いくわよ！」

Kana enjoyed the liberated feeling she had when wearing nothing at home. She'd strut around the cage, and the starving Haruo would become transfixed by her carnal buttocks. Kana, in turn, would give him everything from her body. Even when she had to fart, she would let loose in his mouth. She had never felt such superiority in her whole life. But Kana wondered if it was fair to keep these pleasures all to herself. And so a new dream began to sketch itself in Kana's mind.

Kana approached the cage, yanked tight Haruo's collar, and spoke. "I have to go. It's all built up. You'd better drink it up. You like drinking it, don't you? But my, haven't you lost weight these days? I just can't see you lasting very long in this state."

"It's my life's greatest pleasure to live as a slave. It's my truest desire to die as your personal toilet."

"Snap to it, then. I need your mouth at my *oshiri* hole."

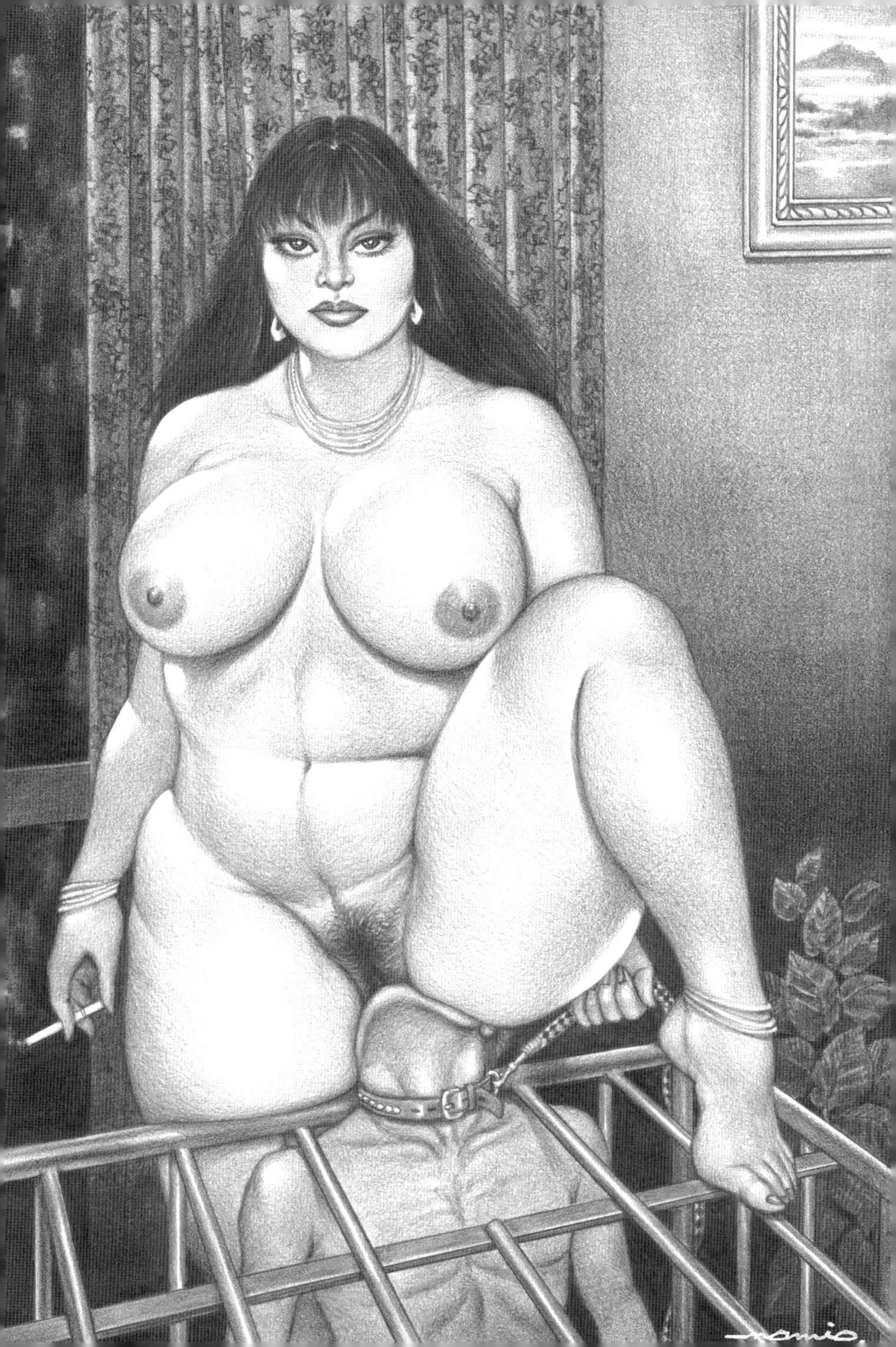

加奈は食事を摂りながら、春男にゆっくりと栄養を与えられるよう、檻の上に便座を取り付けた。そうしてコーヒーとともに、懸命に自分の排泄物を食べる春男の愛おしさを味わった。
「たっぷりお食べ。春も食べるのが巧くなったわ、さすがね。まだ残っているから吸い出してごらん。そう、もっと。う〜ん、気持ちいい」
「とっても美味しいです。最近、味がわかるようになってまいりました。幸福です、加奈様」
「世の中、美が絶対なのよ。美しい私の便器になったお前は、最高の幸せ者ね」
しかし、10日もすると、人間便器は目に見えて弱ってきた。春男に死なれては元も子もない。が、春男は加奈の排泄物しか受け付けない。
「困ったわね、春。このままだと本当に死ぬよ」
「お許しください。すでに加奈様には遺書を書いておきました。私の財産はすべて加奈様に差し上げます。私には妻子もなく、加奈様しかいません。どうぞ、ご心配なく。最高に幸せです」
「フフフ、わかったわ。ほら、口をお開け!」

So that she could slowly pass him nourishment while she took her meals, Kana fastened a toilet seat to the top of the cage. She could enjoy, at the same time now, a cup of coffee and Haruo's ever delightful diligence in eating her waste.
"Eat it all up. You've become better at eating, Haru, for sure. There's still some more, so suction it out please. There, some more. Yes, that feels grand."
"It's very delicious. Recently, I've developed a better appreciation of Mistress Kana's taste. I am so very satisfied, Mistress."
"In this world, nothing compares to beauty. Now you're the toilet for the beautiful me, you must be the happiest man alive."
But, by the time ten days had passed, the human toilet was visibly weak. If Haruo died on her, it would be a total loss for Kana. But still, Haruo would accept only her bodily wastes.
"I'm troubled, Haru. If we keep up at this, you really will be a goner."
"Please forgive me for my audacity, but I've gone ahead and drawn up a will. I am leaving Mistress Kana my entire estate. I have no wife, nor children. Mistress Kana, you are all I have. Please don't worry for me. Now is my greatest happiness."
"Ho! Ho! If you say so… Alright now, boy, open your mouth."

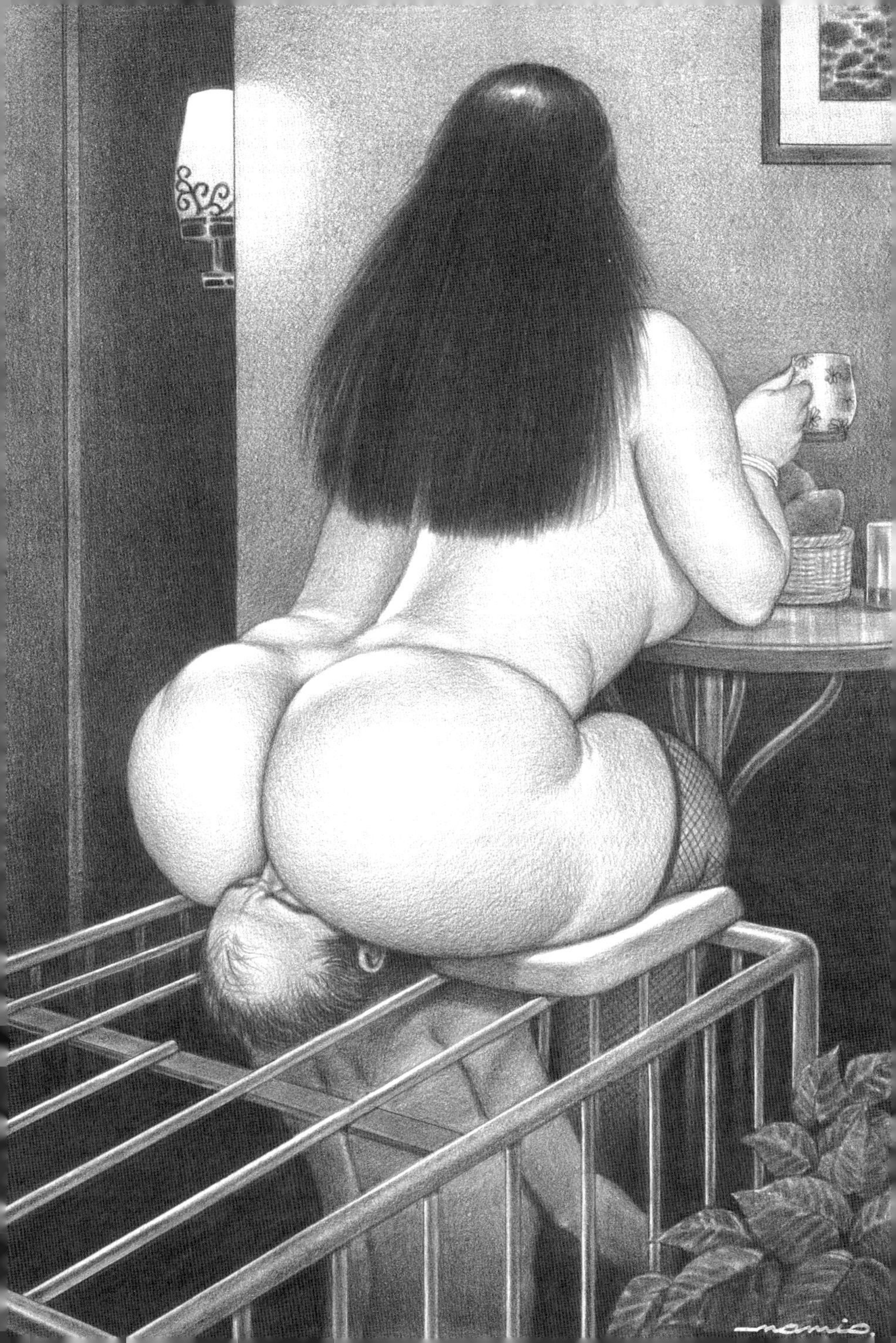
namio.

衰弱を心配した加奈は春男を入院させた。しかし、その甲斐もなく、春男は1週間後に息を引き取った。病院の食事を拒絶し、死ぬまで加奈への誓いを守り、意志を貫いたのであった。

会社を継いだ加奈は、就任挨拶と社長訓示を全社員の前で行なった。男性社員が床に正座し、女性社員が新たにデザインされた制服に身を包み整列する前に、増々豊満に輝きを増す加奈が登場すると、待ち受ける秘書課の田中の顔に腰を下ろした。田中は椅子となり、訓話の間、全身で加奈を支えるのである。すでに辞令が下り、男性社員は平社員に降格、女性は役職に就いた。

「私の方針に不満があれば、今すぐ辞めてもらっていいのよ。私の下で働く限り、絶対服従を誓いなさい。そして女性社員は皆さんは自分を更に美しく磨いてください。社名は美人堂から（株）KANAに変更し、製造ラインは全廃、外注に切り替え、品質管理と品質向上に徹します。もちろん、工場の従業員は有効活用します」

Worried over his weakened state, Kana had Haruo admitted to the hospital. But the concern came too late, and within a week, Haruo had breathed his last. Refusing hospital food and keeping his vow to Kana, Haruo was faithful to his passion until the very end.

Kana took over the company. The Inaugural Welcome and Company Address were held in front of a full assembly of all employees. The male employees sat on their knees on the floor, while the female employees stood in formation, sporting their newly designed uniforms. Before them, an even more voluptuous Kana appeared and rested her hips upon the waiting face of Mr. Tanaka from the Secretarial Section. Mr. Tanaka's function was now as a chair, and for the duration of the Company Address, he supported Kana with his entire body. In fact, the announcement had already been made that all male employees were to be demoted to general staff positions, while the women would assume managerial roles.

"If you have any problem with my policies, you can quit right now. But, as long as you're working for me, I demand your complete submission. Now, lady employees, I want each and every one of you to transform yourself into your most beautiful. The company is changing its name from Lady Luster to KANA Ltd. We will be abolishing all production lines and outsourcing our production. We'll be devoting ourselves, instead, to quality control and to quality improvements. And, of course, our factory employees will remain effectively utilized."

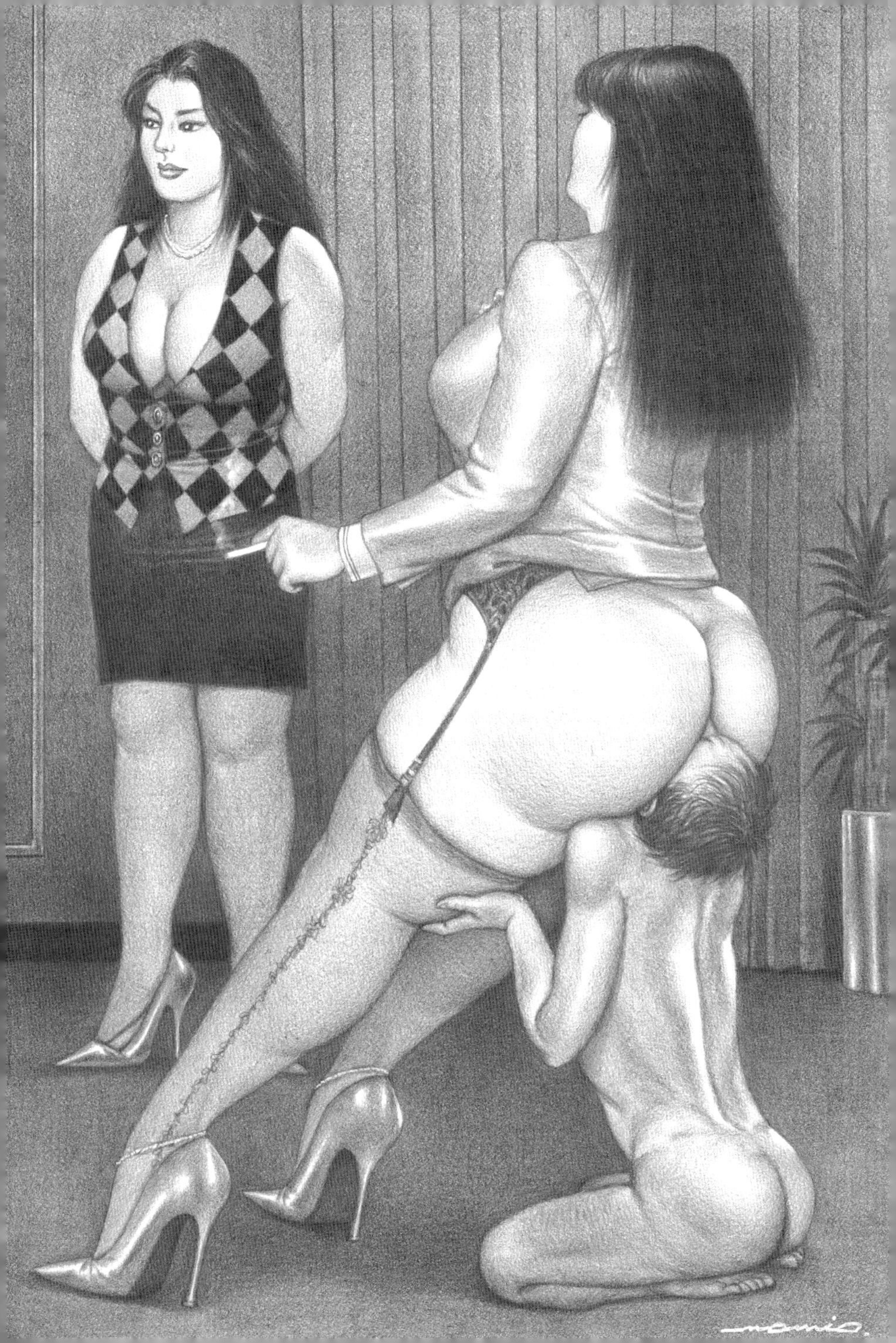

工場廃止による経費削減と、徹底した品質管理の結果、収益は大幅に伸び、女性社員は美しさを増し、男性社員に君臨した。

業務部の田中礼奈部長は、部下の吉本を教育部室に呼び出した。

「服をお脱ぎ!」

礼奈は裸の吉本に首輪をつけリードの先を柱に固定すると、そこに跨がり、下半身で吉本の顔を圧迫した。吉本が顔を真っ赤にして堪えていると、いつの間にか礼奈の手にはムチが握られていた。

「吉本、どうしてこんな目に遭うかわかる? わからないなら、体に教えてやるわ」

苦しみもがく吉本にムチが振り下ろされる。首と手を拘束されて吉本の体は小刻みに震えた。

「君のせいで新製品に欠品が生じて、お得意様から苦情があったのよ。えっ? わかった?」

礼奈のムチが容赦なく吉本の背中を打ち続け、やがて吉本は崩れ落ちた。

「よし、許してあげる。失神の手前だったわね。お舐め。このまま気持ちよくさせてごらん!!」

The cost efficiencies achieved through outsourcing production together with the quality control campaign meant a dramatic increase in profit. KANA Ltd.'s women employees grew in their splendor and lorded over their male counterparts. Tanaka Reina, Section Head for Operations, called Mr. Yoshimoto to the Section's Education Room.

"Off with your clothes." Reina put a collar around the naked Yoshimoto's neck, and tied him with a leash to a pillar. Straddling him, she used her nether parts to squash his face. Yoshimoto's face grew redder and redder as he withstood the pressure, when, as if out of nowhere, he could see the whip in her hand.

"Yoshimoto, you know why you deserve to be treated this way? Your body is the tool I'll use to teach you." The whip descended on Yoshimoto, who writhed in pain. His head and his hands fixed in place, it was his body now that trembled. "The defects in the new product are your fault, aren't they? We got complaints from some of our most loyal clients. Do you understand?"

Reina's whip mercilessly crisscrossed Yoshimoto's back, until finally, Yoshimoto caved in under her. "Alright, I'll forgive you this time. You're about to faint, aren't you? So, go ahead and lick. Make me feel good."

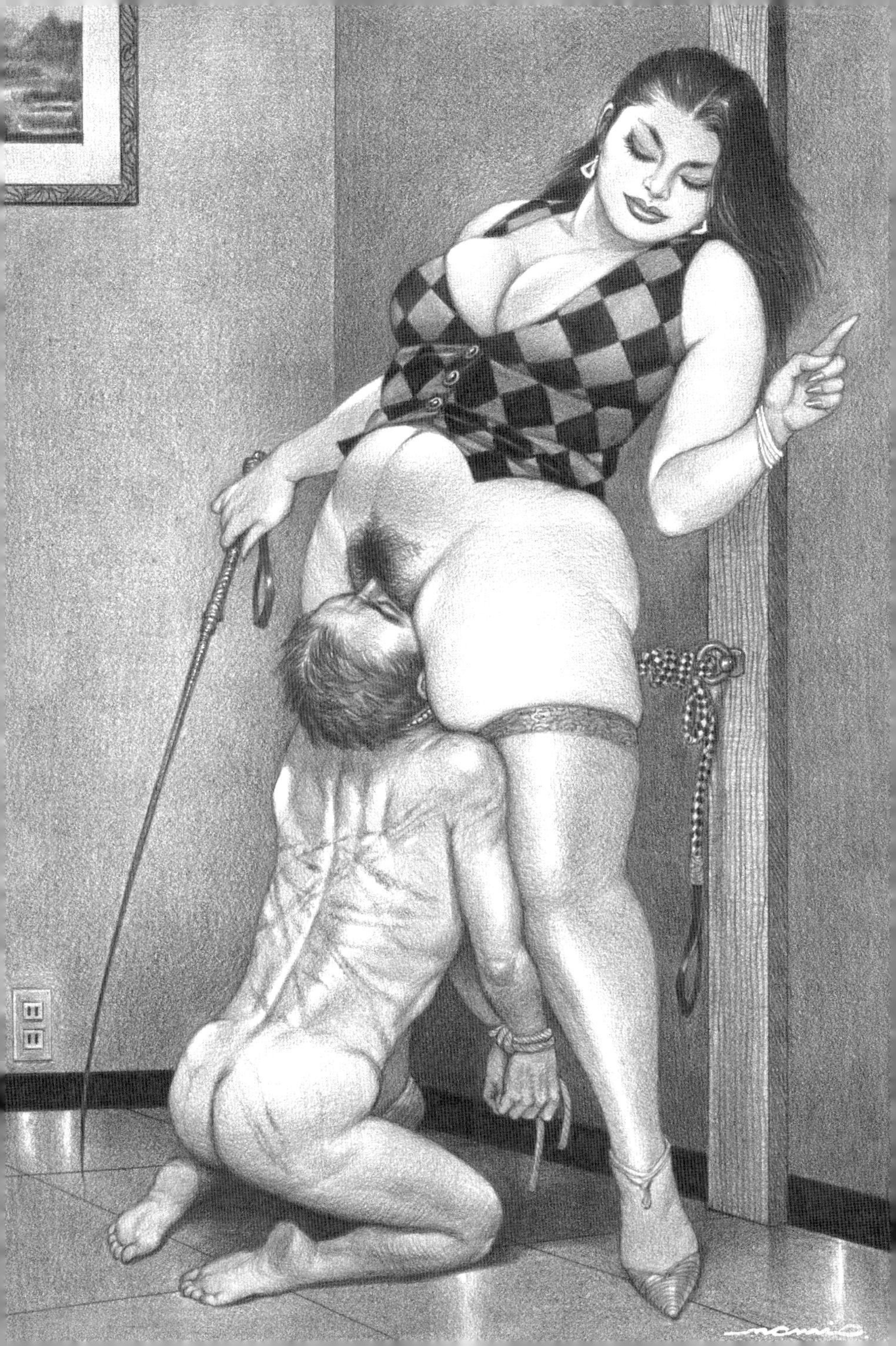

男性社員はすでに女性社員の忠実な奴隷と化し、厳しい命令にも、不思議と悦びを感じるようになっていた。そこで、更に服従心を向上させるため、加奈の提案で、トイレットペーパーを廃止し、代わりに、男性社員が日替わりでトイレに固定されることとなった。
品質管理部長の羽田由美がトイレに入ると、前課長の前田光一が固定されていた。
「あら、前田じゃない。奇遇ね。面白そうだわ。ほら、口をお開け!!」
ペッ!!とツバを吐き、前田の目の前で、パンティを下ろし、用を足すと、指差して命じた。
「上を向いてそこに寝なさい!! さ、早く」
前田があわてて仰向けに寝ると、由美の巨大なヒップが迫ってきた。
「さあ、お舐め。前田でもペーパーの代わりになるのかしら。全部吸い取るのよ。元上司に跨がって後始末をさせるなんて、最高の気分よ、フフ。さあ、次はお尻の穴をきれいにするのよ」
口に密着させると、由美は下腹に力を入れた。
「あら、ウンチが残っていたわ。ほら、お食べ」

Thus, the company men were transformed into the faithful slaves of the women employees. Before long, they began to feel a surprising pleasure at even the most demanding of commands. To increase their sense of submission, Kana suggested a ban on toilet paper; the male employees, it was decided, would take turns being fastened to the toilet for the day. Haneda Yumi, Department Chief for Quality Control, entered the toilet where former Section Chief, Maeda Koichi, had been secured.
"Look who we've got here! Isn't that Maeda? What a pleasant surprise! This does seem fun now, doesn't it? Now, just open your mouth." Yumi spat upon him. And then, right before the lowly man, she dropped her panties, did her business, and ordered: "Lie right there on your back. Come along!" Maeda hurried into position facing upwards on his back as Yumi lowered her massive hips towards him.
"Go on, now, and lick! I hope you'll make good paper. You have to suck it all in. What a thrill it is to straddle my former boss and watch him get his just deserts. Ha! Ha! Ha! Next, you've got to clean my *oshiri* hole." Yumi pressed in close upon the mouth, and strained her bowels.
"Oh! I've still got some more poo in there. Come on now and eat up."

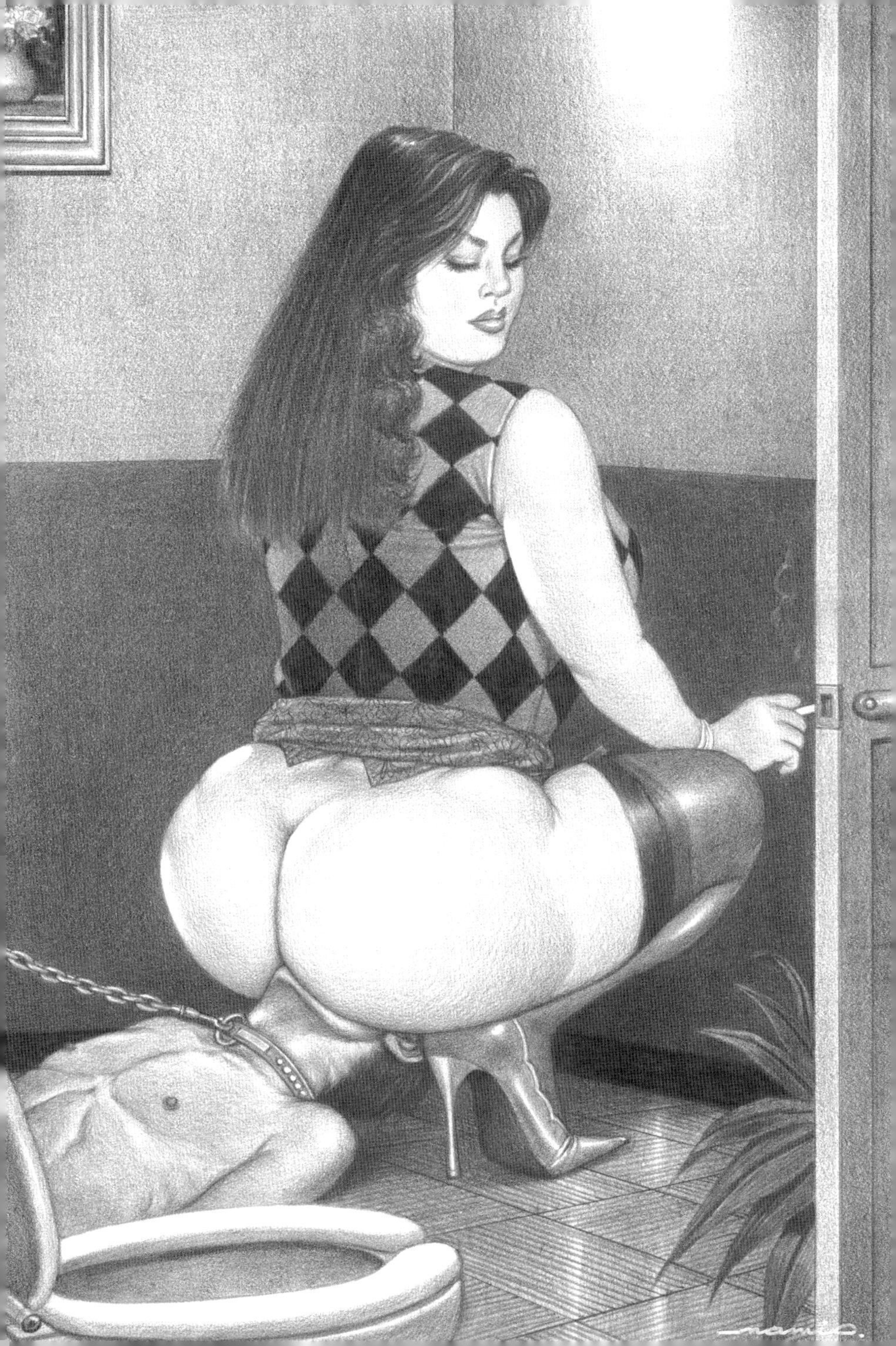

男性社員にとって女性社員全員が上司であり女王様である。しかし、中でも大原社長の存在は唯一絶対であり、女神様であった。
従来の社長の椅子は取り払われ、人間椅子が設置された。椅子の脚に男の両手が固定され、宙吊りのまま加奈社長のヒップを胸と顔で支えるのである。しかし、どの男も120kgの肉が漲る加奈に、2分ほどで悲鳴をあげて失神してしまう。仕方なく男の背中にベルトをあてて補強することにした。
「社長、椅子の調子はいかがでしょうか?」
「最高の座り心地よ。必死に私のお尻を支えているかと思うと、愛おしさと優越感が増すわ。それに、このままトイレになるのが便利ね。ようやく男性社員たちが完璧な便器になったわ。ところで、ビューティ・サロン開発は、進んでいるかしら」
「ハイ、予定通り男たちの教育も含めて順調です」
「楽しみだわ。それから、この男を交代させてちょうだい。失神しているようよ、ホホホ……」

For the male employees, the women employees had become both Bosses and Mistresses to be obeyed. But amongst them all the President Ohara Kana was unique and absolute. She was a Goddess to the men.
The former President's chair was replaced with a human chair. The man's two arms would be secured to the legs of this new kind of chair, and President Kana's body would seemingly float midair, supported by the man's chest and face. But, bearing Kana's resplendent 120 kilograms, no man could last more than two minutes before sounding a shriek as he passed out. There was no alternative, then, but to add a reinforcing strap behind the man's back.
"President Kana, how is your chair?"
"As comfortable as could be. When I think how it's so desperately supporting my *oshiri*, I feel so protective of it and so superior too. And it's especially convenient when you need the toilet. It's taken a while, but finally the men in the company have become the perfect toilets for us. But, on to something else, is everything on track in Beauty Development?"
"Yes. Everything, including the men's education, is moving along fine."
"Excellent. I'm looking forward to seeing what you'll come up with. And, by the way, can you have this man replaced? It seems he's gone and fainted on me. Tee hee hee!"  [120 kilos = 265 lbs]

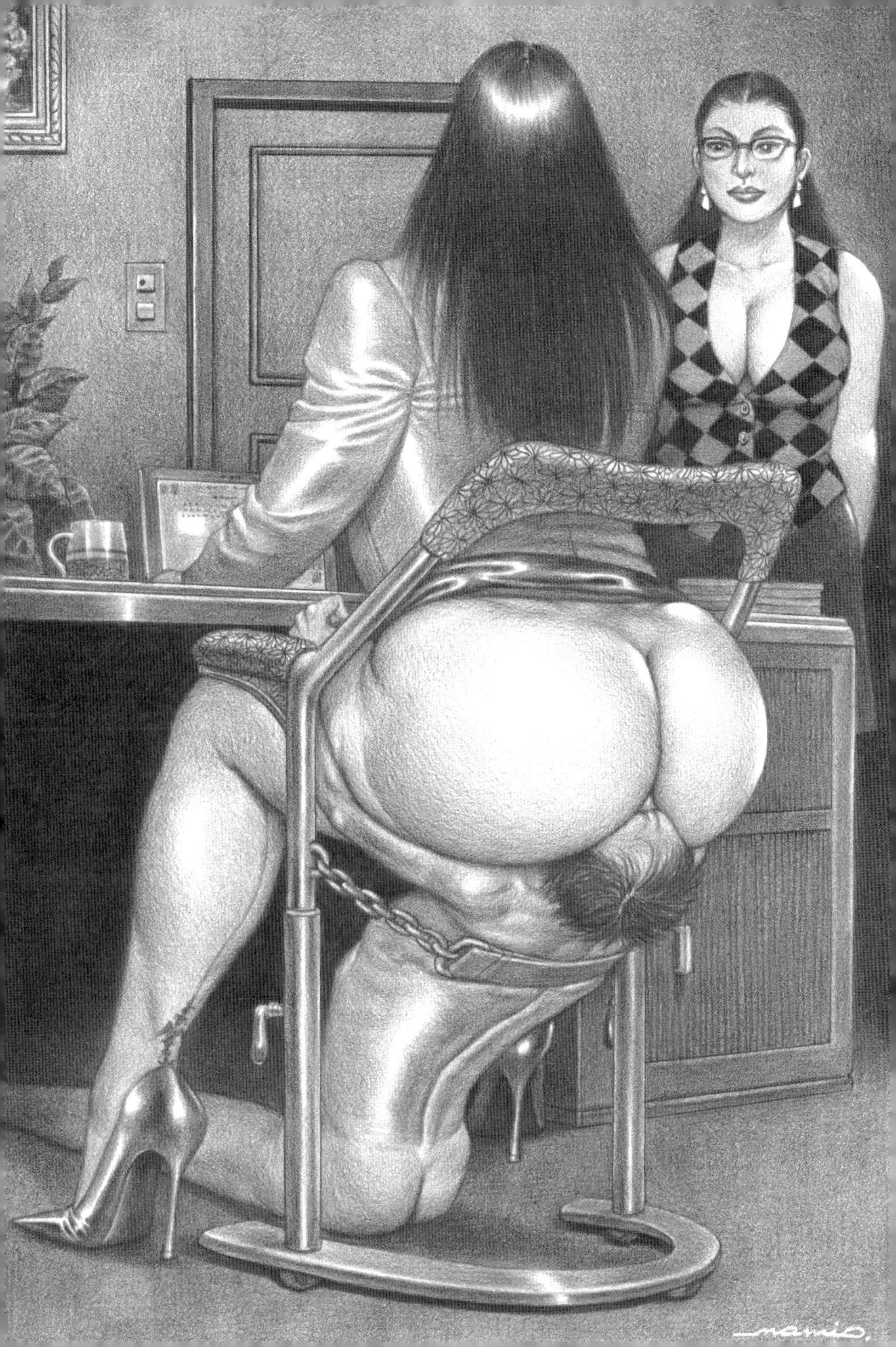
namio.

徹底した合理化で収益をアップさせた加奈は、懸案のビューティ・サロンをオープンした。
お披露目にあたり、社長の加奈自身が広告塔となり、テレビや新聞で、圧倒的なボディを誇示した。果たして思惑通り、予約が殺到した。
多くのビューティ・サロンと違い、サディスティック・ビューティを銘打ったサロンはこれが初めてである。世間一般の"美しく瘦せる"概念を覆し、心身ともに豊かになるのが加奈のサロンの目的である。
女子大生の今井京子が個室に案内されると、小さな椅子に頭を乗せて男が固定されていた。
「お嬢様、下着をお脱ぎになって、顔の上にお座りください」
「いいんですか。可哀想な気がするわ」
「ご安心ください。この男は訓練してありますから、着席したら手足を浮かして、バランスをとって下さい」
「ウワー、すごく面白い。気持ちいいわ。でも、この男の人泣いている、フフフフ……楽しい」

Kana's unyielding rationalization of the business translated into an expanding personal income, and so Kana decided to open a long dreamed of beauty salon. To spread the word, Kana became her own advertising copy. She flaunted her overpowering body on television and in the newspapers. And, just as she expected, the customers came in droves.
Sadistic Beauty—even its unprecedented name set it apart from the run-of-the-mill salon. While most beauty salons operated under a hackneyed ideal of svelte looks, Kana's salon set for itself the opposite: to promote a bountiful spirit in a bountiful body.
University student Imai Kyoko was taken back to a private room in the salon, where she spotted a man, tied down and with his head resting on a tiny chair.
"Miss, would you please remove your underwear and sit down right upon his face?"
"Are you sure about that? I'd feel bad."
"By all means, Miss. This man has been trained for the purpose. Just be sure to raise your legs and arms and balance yourself when you sit."
"How very curious! And it feels so nice. But this man is crying… Tee hee hee! How fun!"

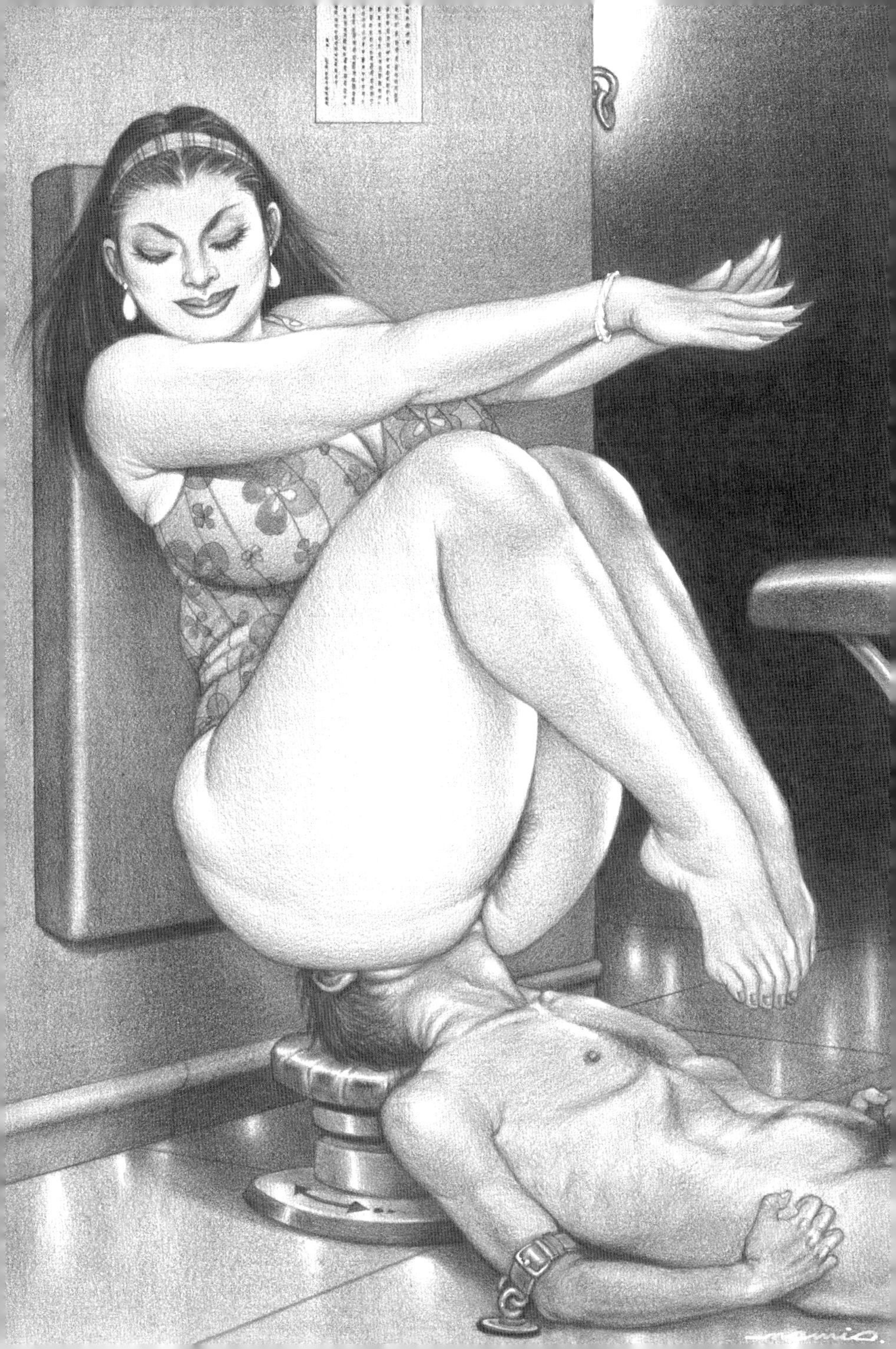

当初は、男の顔の上に座ることをためらった京子だが、お尻の下で苦しみ泣く男にえもいわれぬ快感を覚え、夢中で続けるうちに男を失神させていた。続いて、彼女は顔面快適サドルバイクルームに案内された。下着をとると、顔面サドルにはちきれんばかりのお尻を乗せ、感触を味わう。
「いい感じ。お尻の割れ目にピッタリはまるわ」
「今井様のすばらしいお尻にサドルも喜んでおります。ペダルを踏んでください。だんだん気持ちよくなってきますよ。負荷は画面で調整できますので」
「ああ、お尻が揺れるたびに顔がくっつく。ほら、もっと早くするわよ! ああ、お尻の下で泣き出した。最高! ほら、もっとお泣き!」

Hesitant at first to even sit upon his face, Kyoko felt her senses opening to an exquisite pleasure, and she lost herself to its unrelenting sensations until the whimpering man actually passed out. Kyoko was taken to a neighboring room where she was shown the Facial Feeler Saddle Bicycle. When she got her panties off, she placed her plump *oshiri* right on the bike and again felt the sensations coursing through her body.
"What a great feeling. The Saddle fits perfectly into the crack of my *oshiri*."
"The Sadddle is very happy to be under Miss Imai's wonderful *oshiri*. Now try pedaling, please. It will start to feel better and better. You can adjust the difficulty on the control panel."
"Oh, oh! Every time my *oshiri* heaves, the face rubs against it. Oh, oh, oh!!! I'll try going faster. Now, it's crying under my *oshiri*. This is exquisite. There you go, cry some more!"

"*Shine beautifully, shine lusciously, shine strongly— S. Beauty.*"

美しく.豊かに.強く.
輝きましょう.
　　　　s.beauty

六本木でスナック・ラウンジ2軒を経営する白井淳子は、ストレスでイライラした毎日を送っていたが、サロンの顔面エクササイズにすっかり満足し、続いてエステを受けることにした。施術室でエステティシャンが淳子を迎え入れる。
「ご満足いただき光栄です。男を責めてストレスを解消し、身も心も美しくなっていただくことが我々サロンの最大の目的ですから」
施術ベッドの足元には男が両手を固定された状態で待っていた。
「では白井様、オイルマッサージを行ないますので、腹這いに寝て、男の顔にお尻をつけて、舌奉仕も同時にお楽しみください」
白井淳子の熟したヒップにはさまれ、男は身動きできない。
「ああ、いい気持ち、マッサージも舌の動きも最高よ。この世のものとは思えない快感だわ。ほら、もっとお舐め……」

Shirai Junko had been leading a stressful existence, due largely to the burden of running two bars in Roppongi. But, since she'd become so taken with the Facial Exercises provided at the Salon, she decided to try some of their beauty treatments too. The aesthetician greeted Junko in the treatment room.
"I'm delighted to hear you've been so pleased. More than anything, our Salon wants you to achieve a beautiful spirit in a beautiful body—which you can do by relieving your stresses on a man."
Inside the treatment room, a man was waiting, his two hands attached to the foot of the bed. "So, Ms. Shirai, since we'll be giving you an oil massage, I'd like you to lie on your stomach. If you put your *oshiri* just on this man's face, then you can enjoy tongue service from him at the very same time."
Pinned between Shirai Junko's ample hips, the man couldn't budge an inch. "Ahh, that is good. The massage and his moving tongue are in perfect tandem. It's out of this world, this pleasure… Come on, now, lick me more."

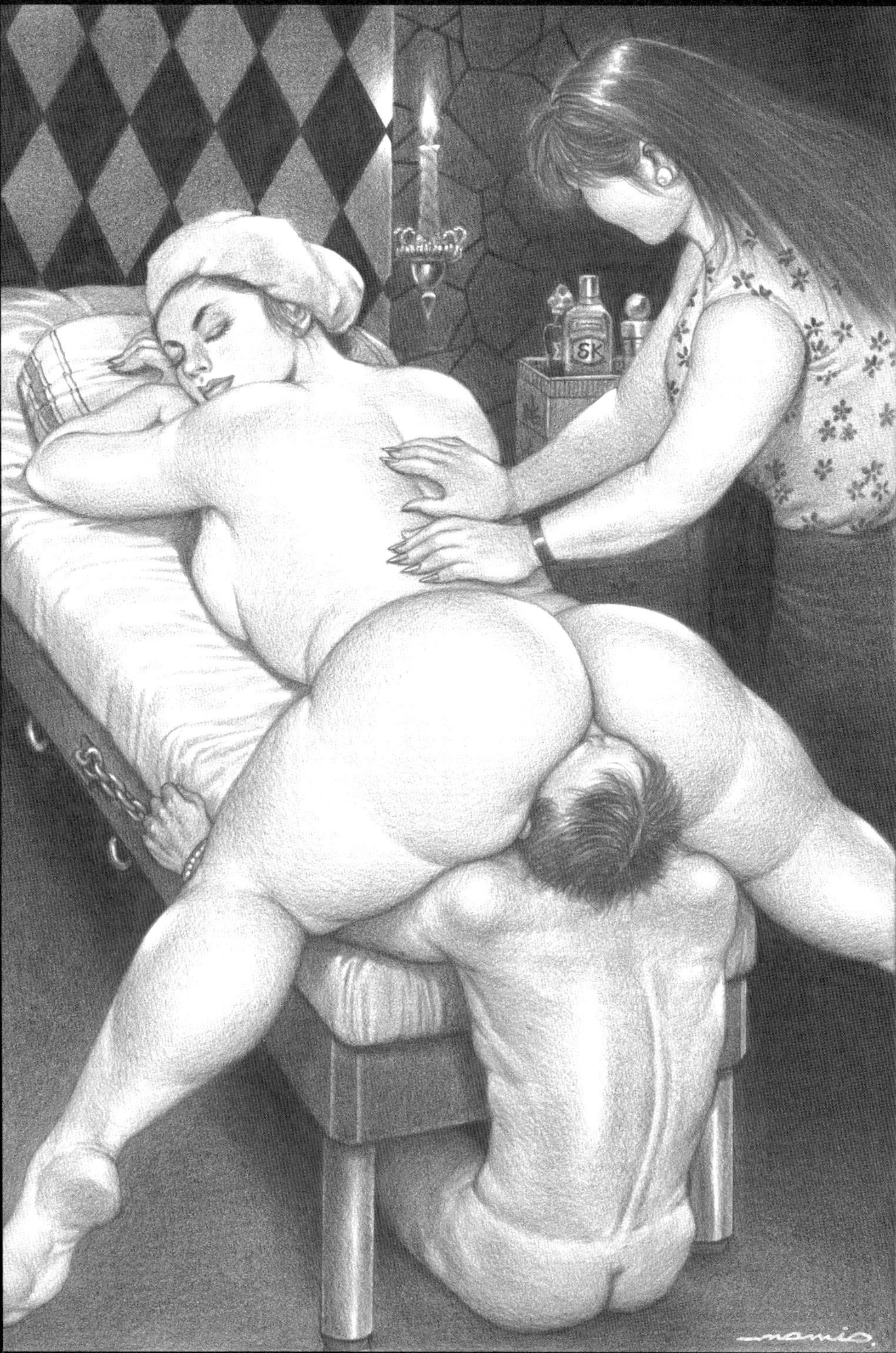
SK

別の施術室では、美人OL中村和子が、正座した男を取り付けたリクライニングシートに腰を下ろす。
「最近、仕事のストレスでドカ食いするから太っちゃって困っているんです」
「決して太っていません。美しさが増したのですわ。でも、ストレスは解消しなくてはなりませんね。さあ、フェイシャルマッサージを受けながら、舌奉仕をお楽しみください」
和子は男の前で、堂々と股を開くと、局部を顔に押し付けた。
「ああ、不思議、平気でこんな大胆な格好が出来るだなんて」
「いい気持ちでしょう？ もっと大胆になって日頃のストレスを発散してください。そして、この東洋式美顔マッサージで更に美しくなりますよ」
「ああ顔も体も最高にリラックスしてきたわ。そこ、気持ちいい。舌がお尻の穴に入ってきた。あ、動いている、ん……快感!!」

In a different treatment room, an office worker, the beautiful Nakamura Kazuko, settled her well-developed hips into a lounge chair—one that had a kneeling man strapped to its front. "Stress from work makes me binge on food. I'm starting to get worried about the weight I've put on."
"You are not in the least bit fat, Ma'am. It's just that there's more to your beauty now. But, we absolutely must do something about your stress. Please enjoy the tongue service you'll get as I give you a face massage."
Without any embarrassment, Kazuko spread open her crotch, and pushed her privates in the man's face. "It's so strange, isn't it? I have no problem at all, showing myself like this."
"Doesn't it feel good? Don't hold back at all; just do as you like and let all your recent stress just disappear. If you can do that, this Oriental Facial Massage will make you that much more beautiful."
"My face and my body both feel so relaxed now. Oh, there! That's good. His tongue went right in to my *oshiri*. I…it's moving. Oh, my God! That's too good!"

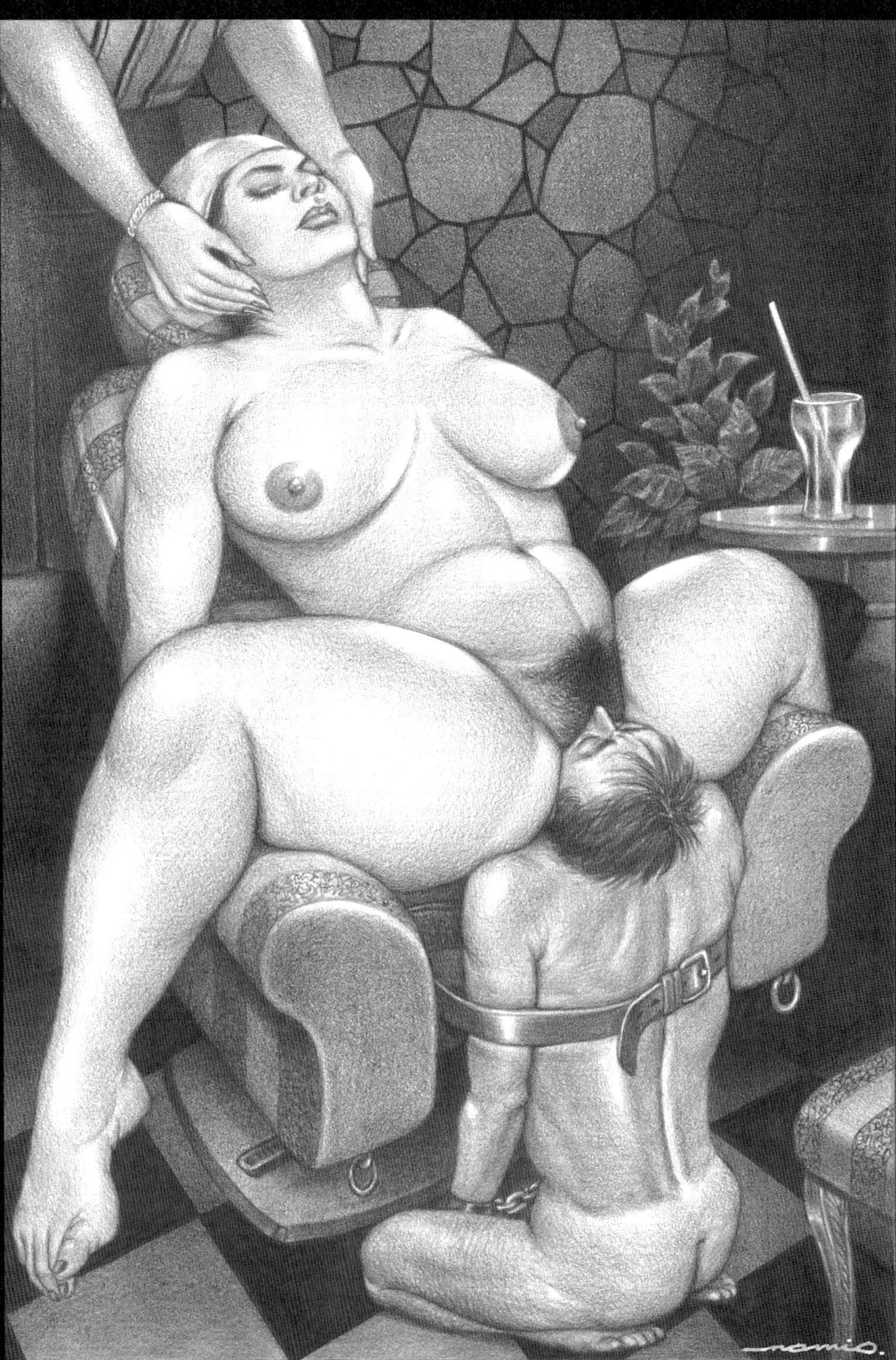
namio.

オープンと同時に、サロンには好奇心旺盛な女性たちが押し寄せ、予約が殺到した。加奈はフロアを拡大し、エステティシャンと奉仕男を増員し、徹底的に訓練した。
常連客でスナックを経営する今井秋代は、加奈とも言葉を親しく交わすようになり、ある時、忠実な奉仕男たちを自分の店でも利用できないか相談した。そして、条件が整い、2人の男のレンタル契約が成立した。
店に出勤してきたホステスのユリはカウンターの椅子に固定された男が秋代のお尻の舌でもがいているのに目をみはった。
「ホホホ、驚いたでしょう。楽しくて気持ちいいのよ。男を責めるって、こんなに感じるとは思わなかったわ」
「でも、可哀そう。死んでしまいますよ」
「殺さないわよ、レンタルなんだから。ねえ、ユリちゃん、この男を利用して女性客にサービスできないか、あなたも考えてちょうだい。ほら、もっと舌を奥まで入れなさい!」

When Sadistic Beauty opened its doors for business, it was inundated with women curious about the new establishment, and a rush for appointments ensued. Increasing the salon's size, Kana took on more aestheticians and service-men, and trained them rigorously.
One regular customer, Imai Akiyo, shared many a confidence with Kana. Akiyo ran a bar, and it occurred to her that she might be able to use a faithful service-man or two in her bar. She consulted Kana. The conditions were discussed, and before long, there was an agreement for the rental of two service-men.
When Yuri, one of the hostesses at the bar, arrived, she was amazed to see Akiyo twisting in pleasure at the tongue of a man fastened to the counter as a bar stool.
"Heh, heh! You must be surprised. It's so much fun, and it feels so good. I never knew that abusing a man could make you feel like this."
"But, he looks so miserable. It looks like he could die that way."
"I'd never kill him. 'Cuz he's here on rental. Say there, Yuri, couldn't you use these men to service our women customers somehow? Give it a thought, will you? You down there! Get your tongue in deeper!"

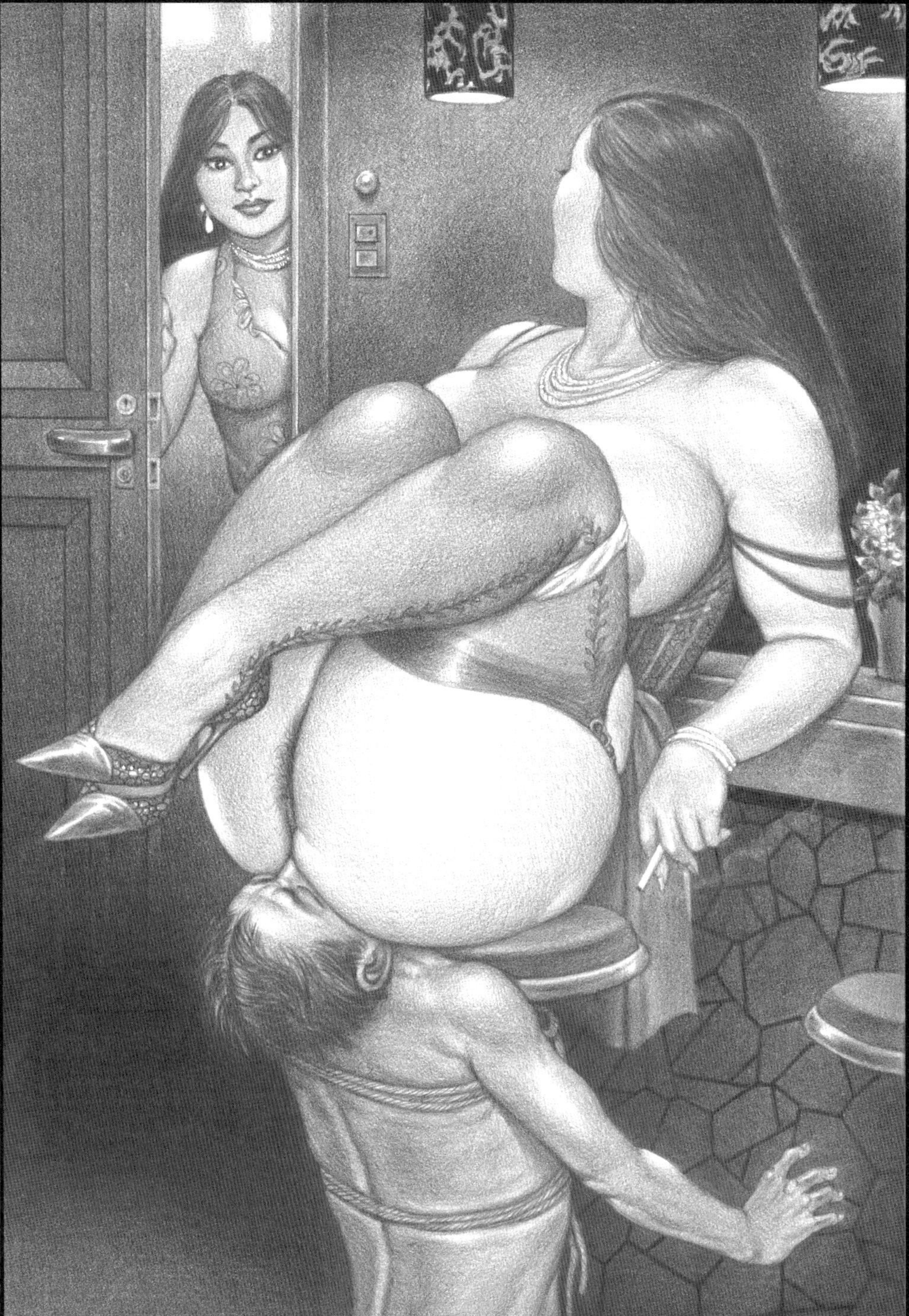

秋代の店では、レンタル男2名の利用方法についてホステスたちがアイデアを出し合った。
── ストレス解消に平手打ちする
── お客様の脚を椅子の下でマッサージさせる
── 憂さ晴らしに鞭で打つ
── 馬にしてお客様をトイレまで運ばせる
── 椅子にしてお客様に座ってもらう
秋代ママが最終決定を下し、椅子として使用することになった。カウンターの下に専用金具を取り付け、男の両手を固定した。果たして、これで、お客様を支え続けることができるであろうか。秋代ママが耐久テストを行なうことにした。スカートを捲り上げ、爛熟したヒップを男の顔に下ろす。
「全体重を預けるから、しっかり支えるのよ」
が、間もなく男が苦しみ出した。
「あら、100kgあるから、ちょっと無理かもね。いいわ、考え直すことにするわ」

The hostesses at Akiyo's bar discussed among themselves proposals for using the two rental-men.
—Slap the rental-men to relieve stress.
—Have the rental-men massage customers' feet under the bar stools.
—Use the whip on the rental-men to get oneself out of a funk.
—Use the rental-men as horses to carry customers to the toilet.
—Use the rental-men as chairs for the customers to sit upon.
It was Akiyo, the bar's *mama*, who was given the final decision, and thus it became the practice that the two men were to be used as barstools. Specially designed metal fittings were attached to the bottom of the bar counter; these were intended to secure the two men's arms. But would their two rental-men really be able to bear the bar's customers for such an extended period? Mama Akiyo decided that an endurance test would be necessary. She lifted her skirt and settled her overripe hips onto one of the faces.
"I'm going to try putting my full weight on you now. Hold me well, you hear boy?" Almost immediately, the sounds of whining could be heard from the man.
"Well, it looks like my 100 kilos are a bit too much for you. We'll have to rethink this."  [100 kg = 220 lbs]

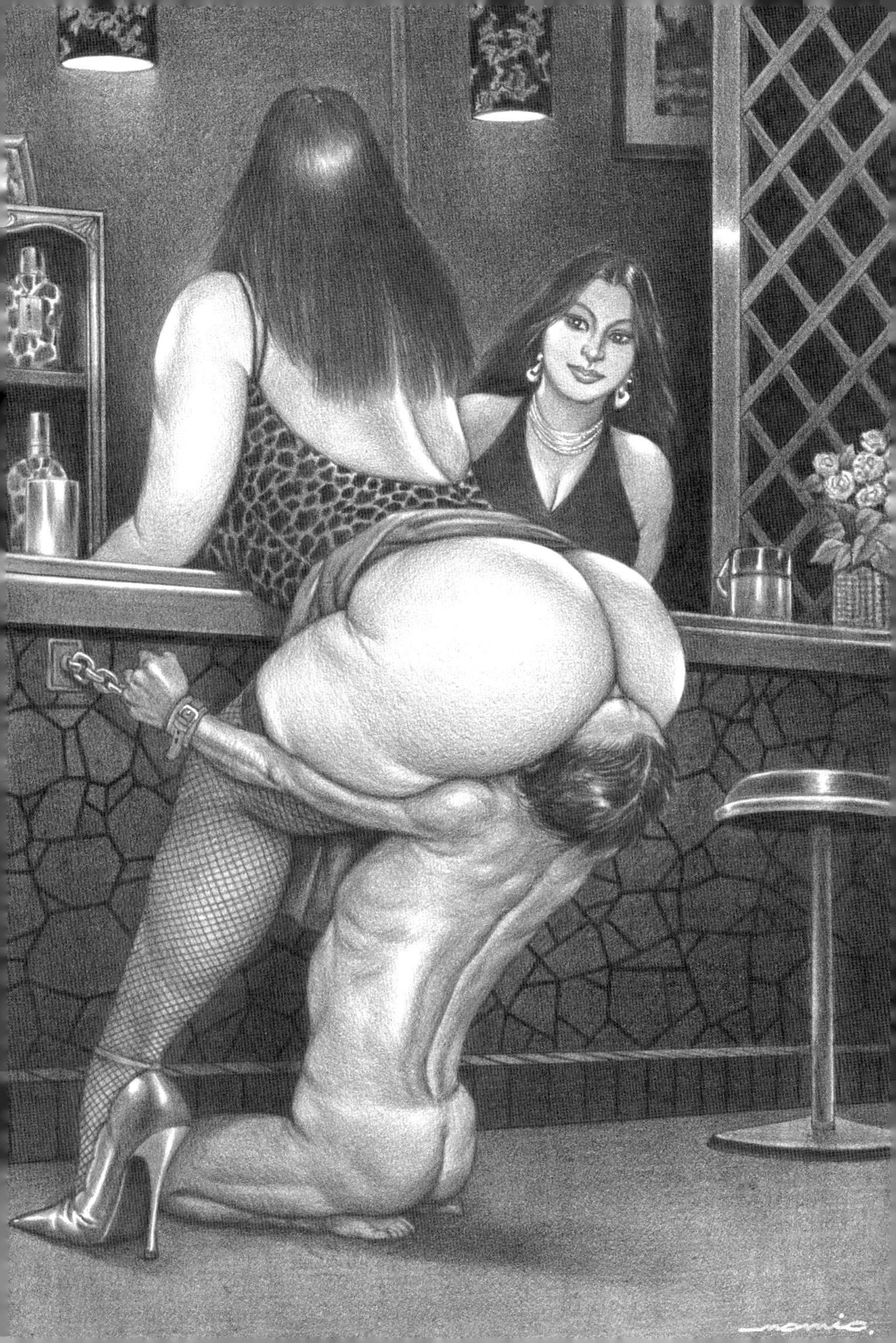

レンタル男を実験台にした試行錯誤の結果、人間椅子第1号が完成した。
重圧に耐えられるよう、男の頭部を革製クッションのついた座面に乗せ、高さを調整可能にし、拘束した手を椅子の脚につないだ。
人間椅子お披露目の日、さっそく噂を聞きつけたOL2人組がやってきた。
2人は戸惑いながらも、ママに促されるままに、パンティを下げると、豊かなヒップを座面に乗せた。
「ごめんね。重いでしょう。でも気持ちいいわ。ちょうど鼻がお尻の割れ目に入って口が穴に当っているのよ。ああ、いい感じだわ」
「男の顔に座ってお酒を飲むって快感。あ、舌が動いている」
「この男たちはよく調教されているのよ。でも窒息しないよう、時々お尻をずらして空気を吸わせてあげてちょうだいね。5分はもつからね」

After a lengthy process of trial and error using the rental men as guinea pigs, Human Chair: Model No. 1 was finally completed. So that he might bear the required weight, the man's head was placed on a leather cushion. His bound arms were tied to the leg of the stool, which could be adjusted for height. The day the Human Chair was unveiled to the public, two female office workers who'd heard rumors of the product came to see it for themselves. At first hesitant, the two lowered their panties at Mama Akiyo's urging and rested their generous hips on the seat.
"I'm sorry, I know I must be heavy for you. But, this does feel good. His nose fits right into the crack of my *oshiri*, and his mouth is right at my hole. My, this does feel nice."
"What an incredible feeling it is to sip your drink as you're sitting on a man's face. Ah, I can feel his tongue moving."
"These men are well trained. But, to prevent their suffocating, do remember to lift your *oshiri* from time to time to give them some air. They can last about five minutes at a time."

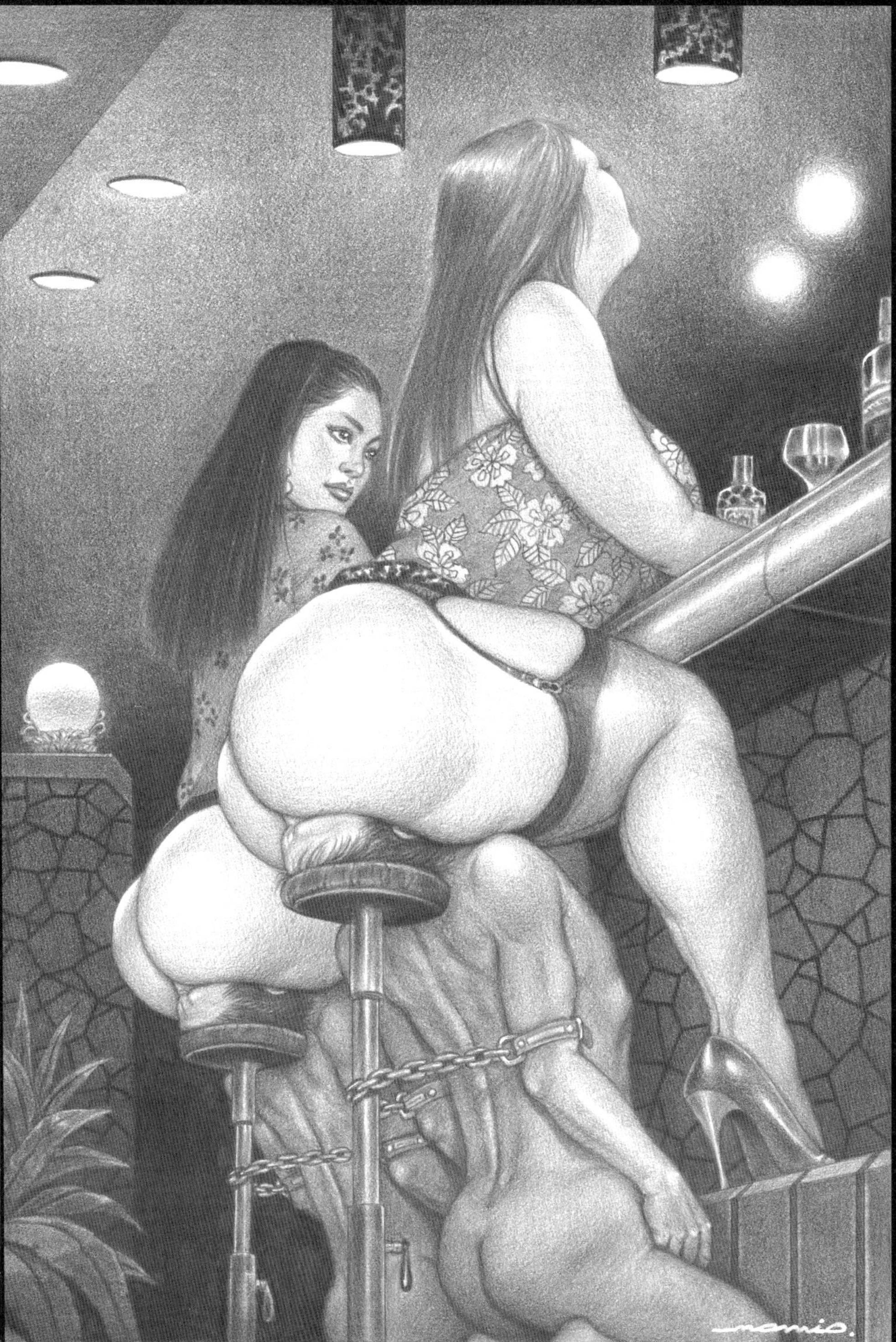

ラグジュアリーな気分でお酒が飲めるとあって人間椅子は人気となり、秋代ママのスナックは増設がおいつかないほど繁盛した。

椅子に座る快感を覚えた者は、さらなる刺激を求めずにはいられない。密かにお尻に密着した口を開けさせ少しずつオシッコを飲ませる行為が散見するようになった。毎晩、閉店後の反省会で、男たちの報告を聞くうちに発覚したのだ。しかし、それなら、思い切って人間便器も設置しようと、ママは便器に耐えうるA級男をレンタルすることにした。そして、希望する女性に、特別室で使用していただくことになった。

美貌の女医、大村育代が特別室に入ると、重厚なヒップを便器男の上に下ろした。

「さあ、ウンチをするわよ、食べられるわね？　まずお尻の穴を丁寧にお舐め……舌を奥に入れるのよ。そう、さあ、いくわよ、ほら、しっかりお食べ!」

The Human Chair allowed the user a sense of luxury as she drank, and soon the Chairs became so popular that Mama Akiyo had difficulty keeping up with the refittings necessary to bring in more units.

But for those who experienced the pleasure of sitting on one of these Chairs inevitably there emerged a desire for something even more intense. Now and then, there were reports of women who discreetly fed the mouth attached to their *oshiri* their pee little by little. The men would report this use in the nightly reviews that followed closing-time. Mama Akiyo decided that it made sense to go ahead and install a human toilet; she decided that should would rent some Class A service-men who could be used as toilets. For the women who wanted to use these men, Akiyo built a special room.

Omura Ikuyo, a doctor and a woman of rare beauty, entered the special room. She lowered her stately hips onto the toilet-man.

"I'm going to shit now. But, you'll eat it, right? First, I want you to carefully lick my *oshiri* hole. Put your tongue all the way in. Ah, it's coming. Come on, boy, eat it up."

Tidy yourself afterwards with our complementary male tongue-service. Please ring the bell for service.

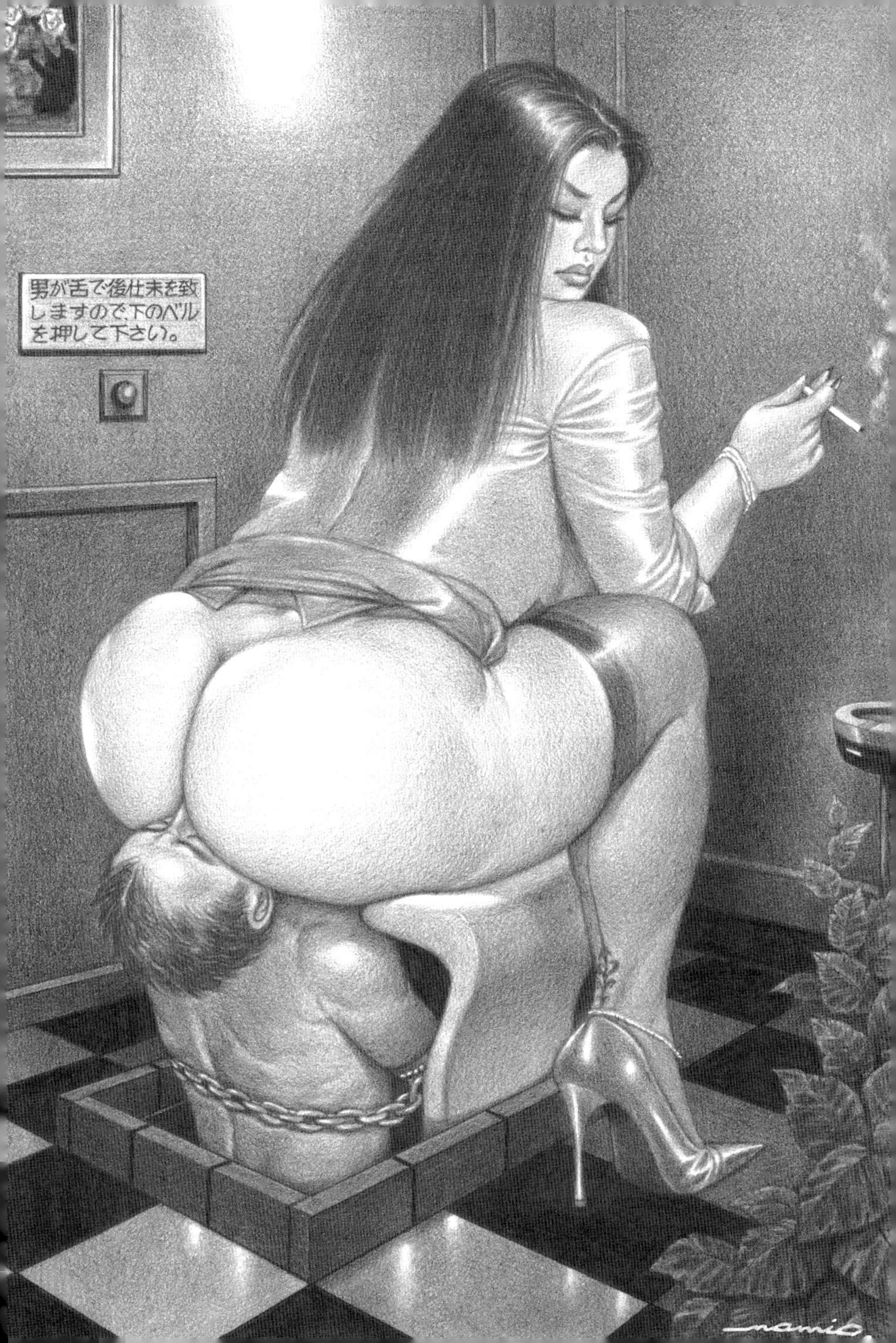
男が舌で後仕末を致しますので、下のベルを押して下さい。
namio

秋代のスナックは話題となり、これを見た他の店もレンタル男の導入を希望したため、男の供給が追いつかなくなった。
そこで加奈は、本格的に男派遣業「女神たちのしもべ」を開始した。男の調教・訓練係の女性を募集したところ、SMクラブの女王たちが集まった。そして、加奈自らがテレビCMでレンタル男の勧誘を呼びかけたところ、M男たちが続々と志願し、美しい調教師たちによる研修が始まった。
「女神たちのしもべ」はオープンと同時に注文が殺到した。美容師の島田恵子も自宅マンションへの派遣を依頼した。
「君が三郎というのね。私は、とてもイライラしているから思いっきりいじめさせてもらうわ。さあ、裸になりなさい!!」
恵子が三郎を後ろ手に縛り、発達した太腿にその顔を挟み、絞め上げると、悲鳴が漏れた。
「まだまだこれからよ。泣いてないで、お尻をお舐め。そう、いい舌の動きだわ……」

Akiyo's bar became the talk of the town. But, when other bars in town attempted to repeat her success by introducing their own rental-men, maintaining a steady supply became a problem. Kana inaugurated a contract male provider service, which she named Minions to the Goddesses. She got together Mistresses from the city's S/M clubs in order to find enough women capable of training and disciplining men. Once she had done that, Kana herself appeared in TV commercials in an appeal for new rental-men. The masochists enlisted themselves, one after another. Once in the hands of their beautiful instructors, the men began their training.
Orders flooded in as soon as Minions to the Goddesses opened for business. A hair stylist, Shimada Keiko, ordered one for personal use in her high-end flat. "Your name is Saburo, I was told. Well, I have to let you know I'm feeling terribly cranky right now, so you're going to have to let me abuse you quite hard. Get undressed."
Keiko tied Saburo's hands behind his back and squashed his face with her prominent thighs. As she began to squeeze, a scream escaped his lips.
"Come, come now, don't cry. We've just started. Have a lick at my *oshiri*. Yes, that is very good tongue-work."

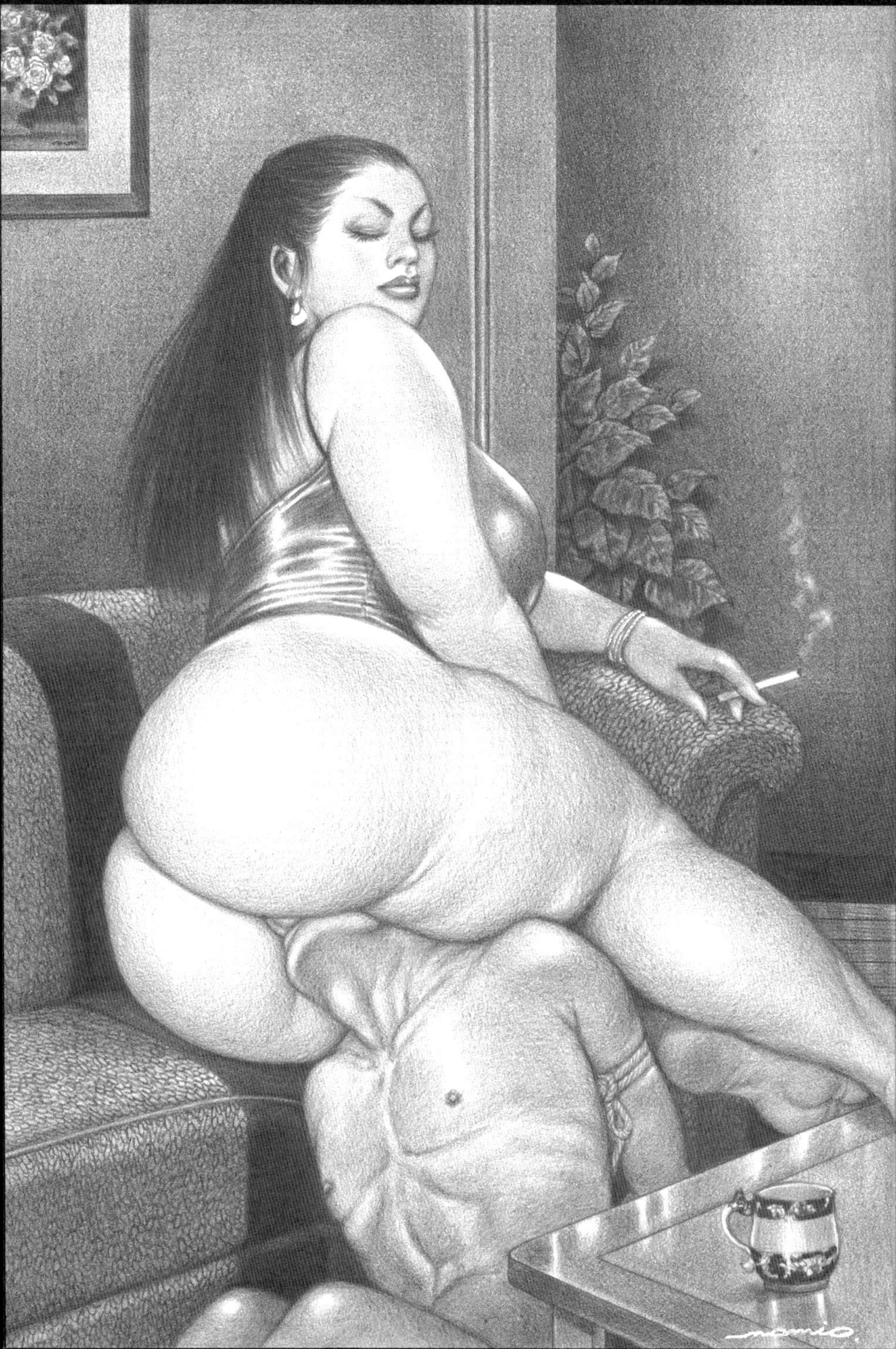

恵子は三郎の舌の動きに酔いながら、更に太腿で締め上げ、もがき苦しむ姿を見ては寝る間を惜しんで快感を貪った。
レンタル男は1日につき2万円、24時間単位で借りるシステムである。期限の明日の夜まで、愉しみ尽くさねばなるまい。
恵子は三郎に、首輪をはめると寝室に引き込み、自身は全裸になり、ベッドに腰をおろすと正座する三郎の前で両脚を大きく開いた。そして、目のやり場に困り下を向いたままの三郎に命じた。
「しっかり目を見開いて、真っすぐご覧。教えてやるわ、お前が舌で奉仕するところよ。さあ、お舐め!! いいと言うまで続けるのよ」
三郎は恵子のはちきれんばかりの太腿の間でカエルのように無様な格好になりながら剛毛を掻き分け懸命に舌を動かし続けた。とろけるような快感に、恵子はそのまま心地よい眠りに落ちっていった。

As Keiko reveled in the movements of Saburo's tongue, she squeezed her thighs harder. Sparing no time for sleep, she indulged herself in the pleasures of seeing him writhe and struggle.
A rental-man could be had for a twenty-four hour period at a rate of 20,000 yen/day. This rental-man needed to be returned by the following evening, so Keiko had to completely satisfy herself before that.
Keiko put a collar around Saburo's neck and dragged him to her bedroom. She stripped nude, dangled herself from her bed, and opened wide her two legs before the kneeling Saburo. Not knowing where he might rest his eyes, Saburo looked down. But Keiko then ordered: "Keep your eyes wide open and look straight ahead. I'll show you right where I want your tongue to service me… Okay, get licking. And don't stop until I tell you."
Saburo made for an ungainly sight as he leaned toad-like between Keiko's thighs, thrusting his tongue back and forth through the bristles of her crotch. Losing herself to a dreamlike bliss, Keiko drifted into a comfortable sleep.

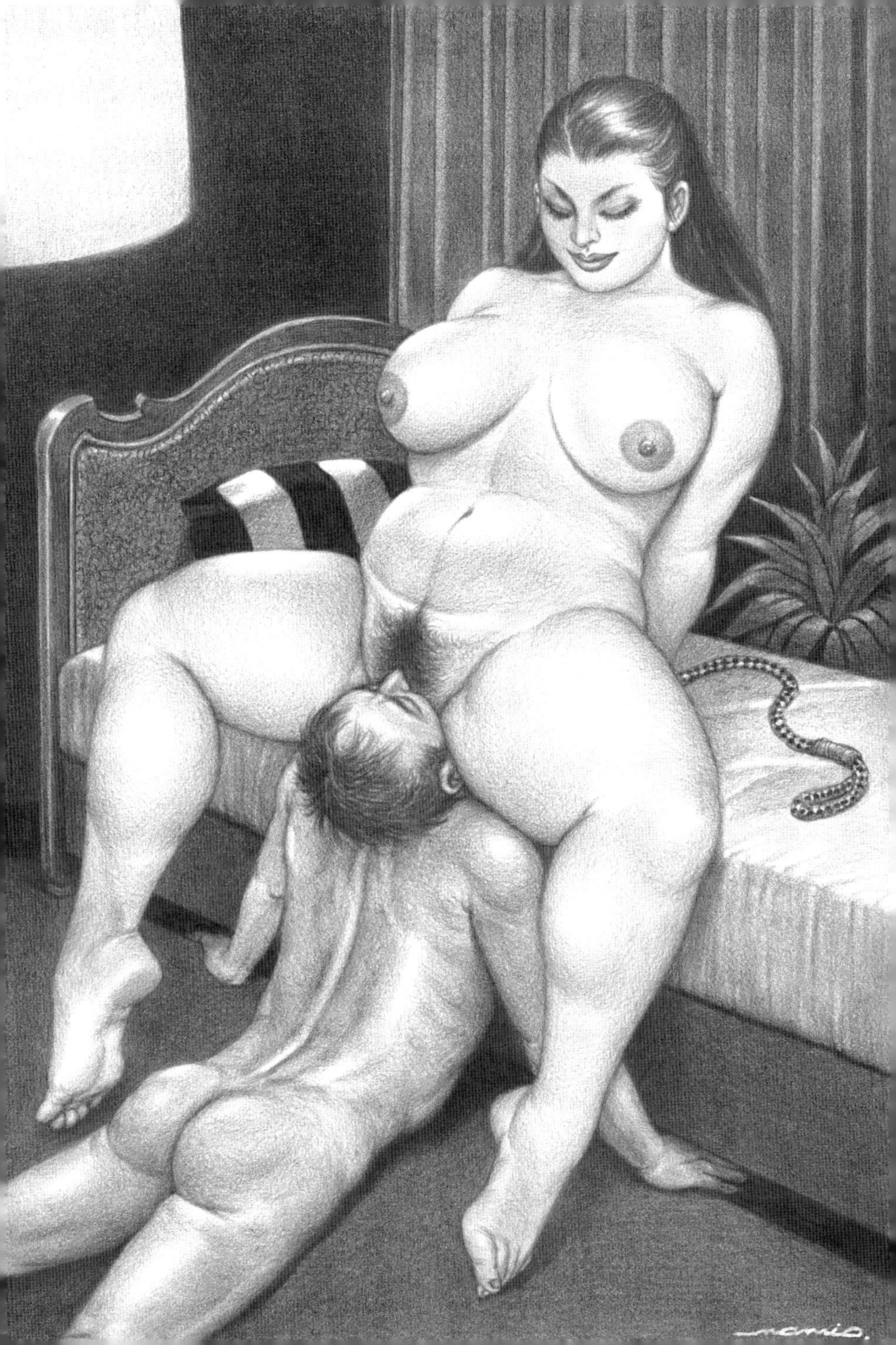

恵子の就寝中も、三郎は太腿に挟まれたまま舌を動かし続けたが、疲労と睡魔に負けてついつい眠ってしまった。翌早朝、恵子が気持ちよく目覚めると、太腿の間で三郎がだらしなく眠りこけていた。
「こらっ‼　起きろ」
恵子は両腿で三郎の首を絞めた。
「私の命令を守れなかったわね。舐め続けろと言ったはずよ」
言うやいなや、恵子は三郎をベッドの下に蹴り落とした。
「本当に申し訳ございません！　ど、どうぞお許し下さい」
「私の命令に絶対服従するなら許してあげてもいいわ」
「はい。絶対服従をお誓い申し上げます」
恵子はリビングの椅子の脚に三郎を縛りつけ、その顔にお尻を乗せて、朝のコーヒーを啜り出した。
「お尻の奥まで舌をいれて、動かしてごらん。あ、そこ、そこ。気持ちいい……あら……？　苦しいの？　もっと苦しむがいいわ、ホホホ」

Sandwiched between Keiko's thighs as she slept, Saburo continued to move his tongue, but he finally gave into his fatigue and sleepiness. When Keiko awoke the next morning refreshed from a good night, Saburo lay sprawled like a log between her thighs, slumbering away.
"Hey, there! Get up!" Keiko squeezed Saburo's neck with her two thighs. "You didn't follow my orders, did you? I thought I told you to keep licking." No sooner had Keiko scolded him than she kicked Saburo off the bed.
"I am so very, very sorry. Please forgive me."
"If you obey my orders completely, then I might."
"Yes, I swear my complete obedience to you, Mistress."
Keiko tied Saburo to the legs of a chair in the living room, and rested her *oshiri* on his face and sipped her coffee.
"Reach your tongue all the way into my *oshiri*. Then, try moving it. Yes, there, right there. It feels good. What? Is that hard on you? I'll be even harder on you, don't you worry!" Keiko chortled.

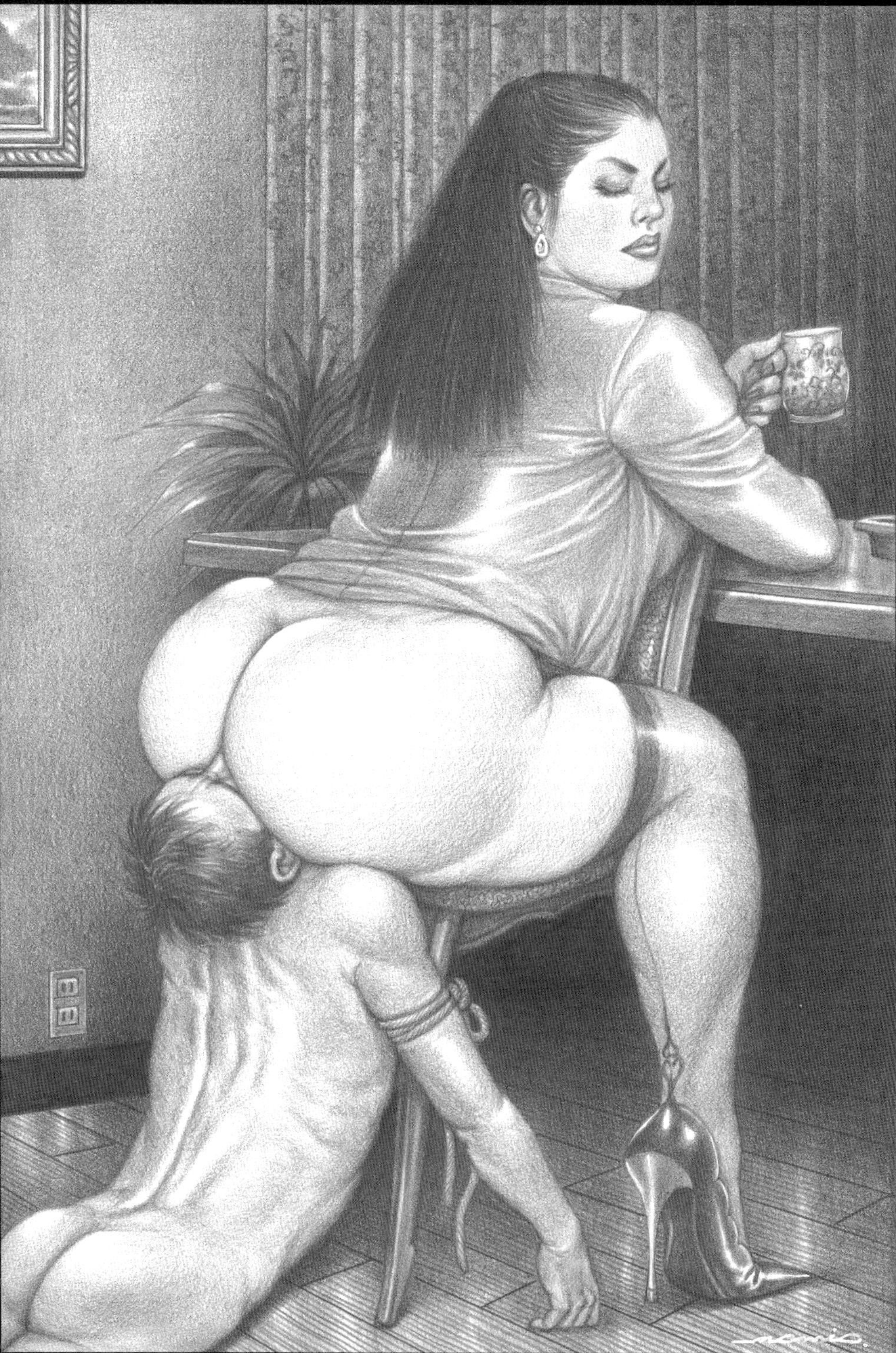

恵子のお尻に埋もれ、舌奉仕するうちに三郎は失神してしまった。気を失うまで奉仕した三郎を恵子はかわいいと思った。
「だらしないわね、ホホホ。でも、まだまだ許さないわよ、私に虐められて、どんな気持ち?」
「気を失って申し訳ございません……。しかし、美しい恵子様のお尻に埋もれて失神するほど責められる幸福にうち震えております」
「あら、虐められて幸福なのね。嬉しいこと。さて、絶対服従すると誓ったわね。それなら、ついていらっしゃい」
恵子はトイレに向かった。
「便座に仰向けに頭を乗せなさい」
恵子は三郎を便器にして腰掛けた。
「ゆっくり、お舐め、そうすると、出やすくなるのよ。さあ、口をお開け!　よく吸うのよ、出るわよ」
恵子はぐっと下腹に力を入れた。
「ああ、お前の口の中に確実に私のウンチが入っていくのがわかる」
恵子は気が遠くなるほどの快感にわなないた。

o66

Buried in Keiko's *oshiri*, Saburo fainted while offering his tongue service. Saburo, who'd been servicing her until the moment he passed out, was becoming for Keiko more and more charming.
"What a lazy performance! Ha! You won't get my forgiveness that easily. How does it feel to get my abuse?"
"I am very sorry to have fainted. But, I'm quivering in excitement at my good fortune: to bury myself in the beautiful Mistress Keiko's *oshiri* and to be abused until I pass out."
"Abuse for you is good fortune, is it? That pleases me to hear. Now, you've promised your unwavering submission. If so, you're to follow me now." Keiko headed for the toilet.
"Rest your head face upwards on the seat." So that she could use Saburo as a toilet, Keiko sat down upon him.
"Now, lick me slowly. If you do so, it's easier for it come out. Go on now, and open your mouth. Suck it out! Yes, it's coming." Keiko strained her bowels.
"Ah, I can feel my shit going right into your mouth." Keiko shivered at the distant pleasure she was experiencing.

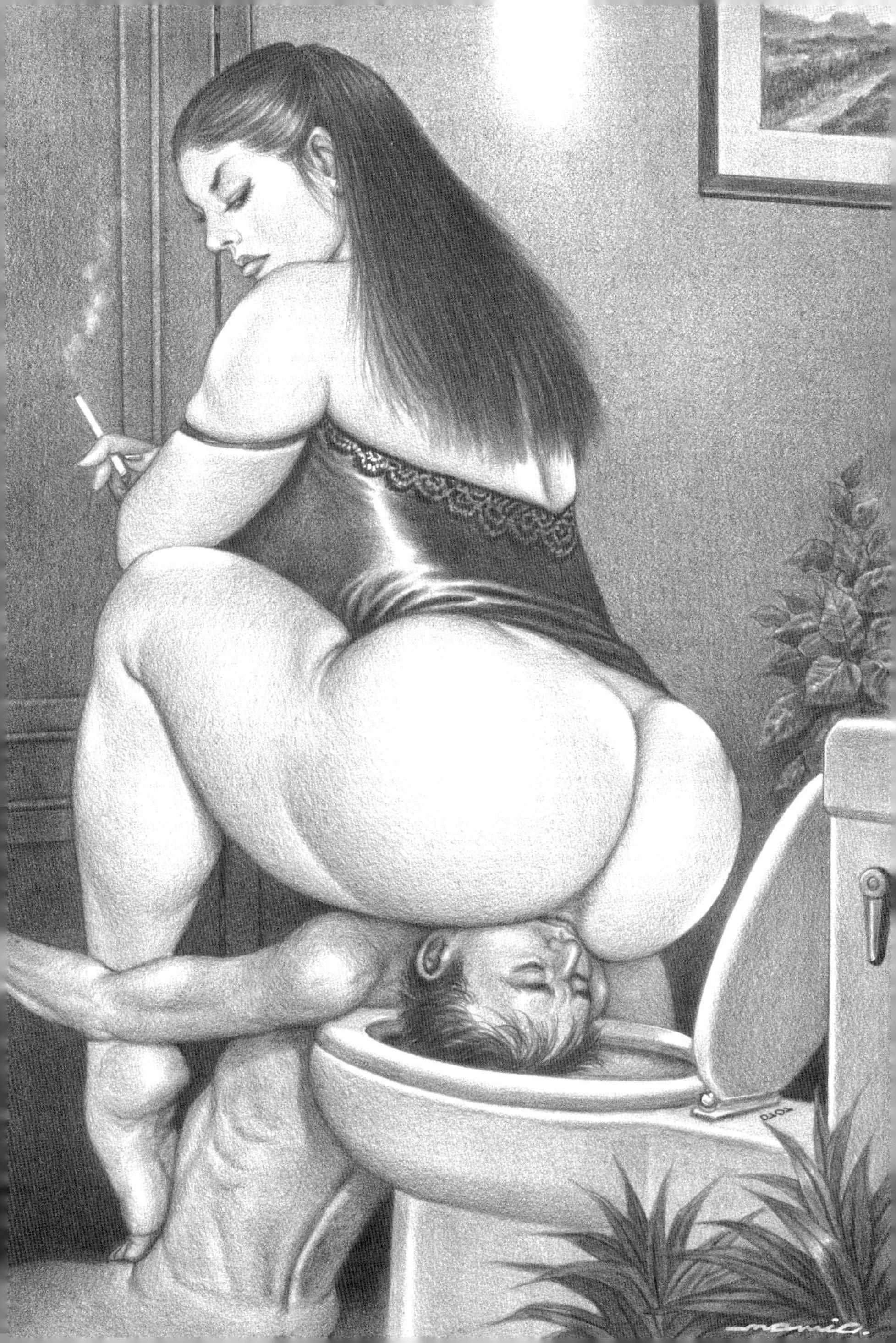

お点前に続き、茶の心得を語り、お稽古を締めくくった茶道師範、田丸美子は、足を崩しながら、お弟子に尋ねた。
「ねえ、敏ちゃん、何か面白いことないかしら？ 最近ストレスのせいか、イライラするの」
町野敏子は目を輝かせながら答えた。
「ありますよ、先生。驚かないでくださいね。奉仕してくれる奴隷男をレンタルするクラブがあるんです。男を思い切り虐めたら、きっとスッキリすると思います」
その夜、美子の豊満なお尻の下には、さっそくレンタルされた浩がいた。
「殺したり、傷つけなければ、何をしてもいいのよね？ ホホホ、心配いらないわよ。思いっきり虐めて泣かせたいだけなのよ！ ああ、いい気持ちになってきた、もっと虐めてあげる」
茶道師範の美子は、苦しみもがく男をお尻の下に敷き、タバコをくゆらしていた。
「あら、泣いているの？ お尻を涙で濡らそうとは、なんて気持ちいい」

Having mastered the rituals of making and serving tea as well as the wisdom behind the art, Tamaru Yoshiko was now a recognized instructor in the tea ceremony. Uncrossing her legs and beginning to unwind after class, she turned to her student, "Toshi-chan, can you recommend something for me? I think it's all the stress I've been feeling lately, but I'm terribly irritable."
Machino Toshiko—called Toshi-chan for short—began to speak, her eyes now sparkling. "There is something, Teacher. Please don't be too shocked, but I've heard there's a club where you can actually rent a male slave to serve you. You'll get over your irritations, I'm sure, after giving a slave a good going-over."
That very evening, Yoshiko was lording her voluptuous *oshiri* over Horoshi, whom she had rented just hours earlier.
"So I can do whatever I like, so long as I don't damage or kill you. Heh, heh, heh. There's no need to worry. I'll be sure to abuse you and make you cry plenty. Since I feel better already, I think I'll just have to abuse you some more!"
Having positioned the man, writhing in pain, beneath her *oshiri*, the tea instructor puffed away at her cigarette.
"Are you crying down there? It feels so good when you moisten my *oshiri* with your tears."

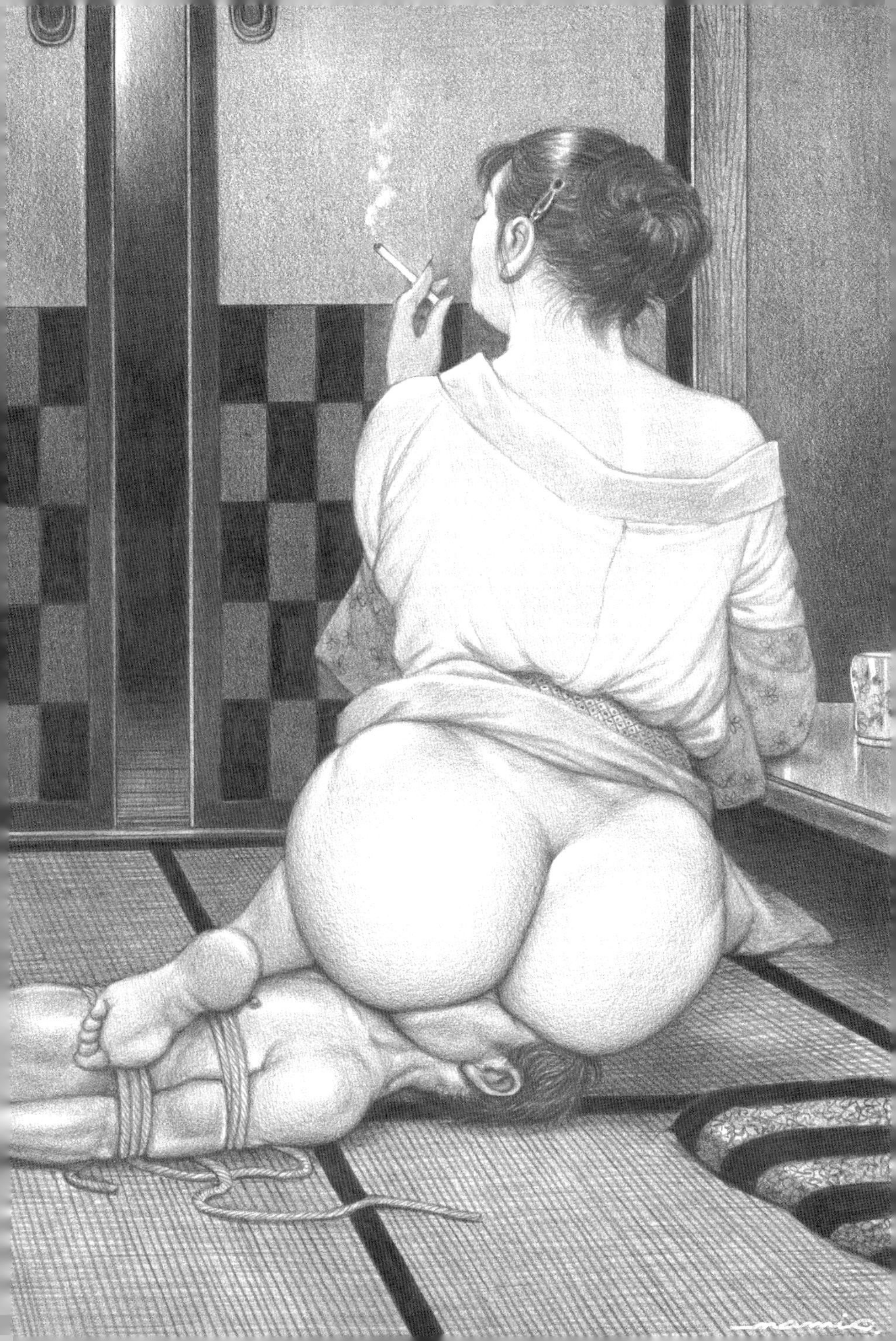

美子は浩をお尻から解放すると、今度は柱にその両手を縛りつけた。
「泣いちゃうなんてかわいい。もっと泣かせてあげるわね」
全裸の美子が、浩の上に股がり、その顔に局部を押しつけると、細い浩の体が弓のように反り返った。美子の繁みに埋もれ、浩の顔が苦痛にゆがむが、美子は容赦なく体重をかけた。
「どうだ、苦しいか、これでどうだ。もっと重くしてやる」
こうして、男を虐め、舌で奉仕させる美子が絶頂に達した瞬間、浩は崩れ落ちた。

Yoshiko liberated Horoshi from her *oshiri* and fastened him by his two hands to a post in the room. "It's so sweet you're crying. I'll make you cry some more."
Completely naked, Yoshiko straddled Horoshi from above and pressed her genitals into his face. A slender man, Horoshi arched backwards like a bow. Buried in her pubic growth, Horoshi's face contorted in agony, but Yoshiko mercilessly pressed down with her body. "How's it feel? Hurts, huh? Well, how's this? I'll put more weight on you."
Abusing this man and making him service her with his tongue brought Yoshiko to an ecstatic climax. Just then, Hiroshi buckled beneath her.

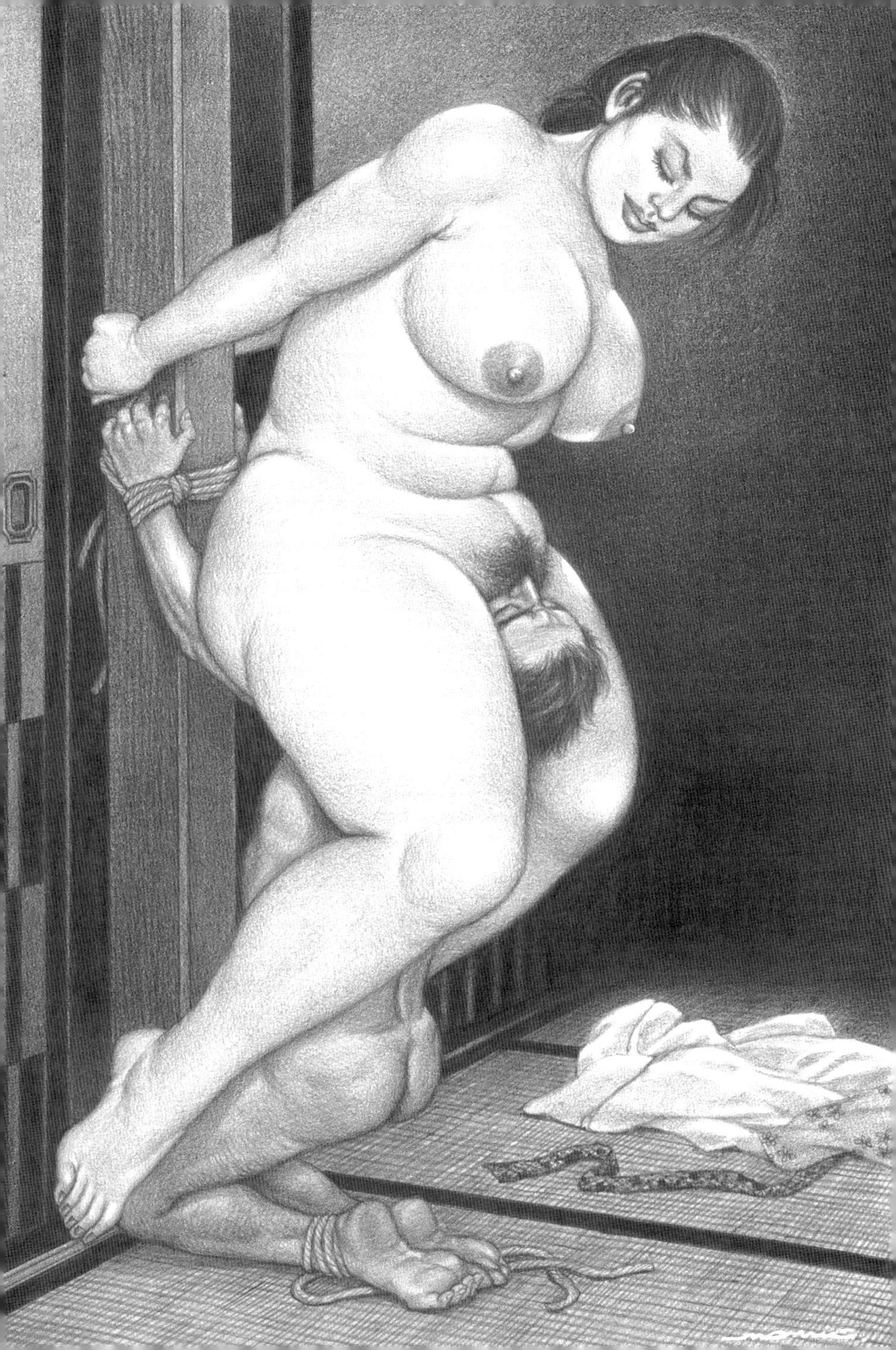

男を責め、泣かせる快感に目覚めた美子は、浩を可愛いく思うようになり、もっともっといじめてやりたくなった。
意識を取り戻した浩に首輪を付けると、寝室に引きずり込んだ。この男の前なら、今まで考えもしなかった大胆な格好も平気でできる。恥ずかしさなんて微塵もない。不思議な感覚である。日頃、弟子たちに茶の道を説く自分が、こんなにも大胆でサディスティックになれるとは。いや、今の姿が本当の自分なのかも知れない。美子は四つん這いになり、浩の前に巨大なお尻を突き出すと、首輪のひもを引いた。
「ホホホホ、しっかり舐めるのよ。あら、オナラが出そう、いいわね、口をお開け!!　するわ〈ヴ、ヴ、ヴ〜〉ホホホホ……最高、今度は奥まで舌を入れて中をお舐め。変な気分……あ、何か、出そう。ほら、出る!!」

Having discovered the delights of tormenting a man and making him cry, Yoshiko found Horoshi more and more charming, and that made her want to abuse him even more. Yoshiko attached a leash to Horoshi's collar and pulled Horoshi, who'd just regained consciousness, to her bedroom. In front of this man, Yoshiko suddenly found herself capable of assuming, without any hesitation, shameless positions that she hadn't even imagined before. She wasn't the slightest bit embarrassed. It was a most curious feeling for her. She was amazed that someone like herself, who had been expounding the sophistication of tea to her students for such a long time now, could become so bold and sadistic. Or, rather, maybe these were her true colors. Yoshiko got on her fours, stuck her tremendous *oshiri* in front of Horoshi, and yanked on his leash.
"Tee hee hee. Lick it well. Oh, I'm going to fart. All the same, just open your mouth. It's coming." Pffftttt. Pffftttt. Yoshiko passed gas. "Oh, that was great! Next time, put your tongue in deeper and lick. What a curious feeling. Oh! Oh! Something's coming. Get set! It's coming."

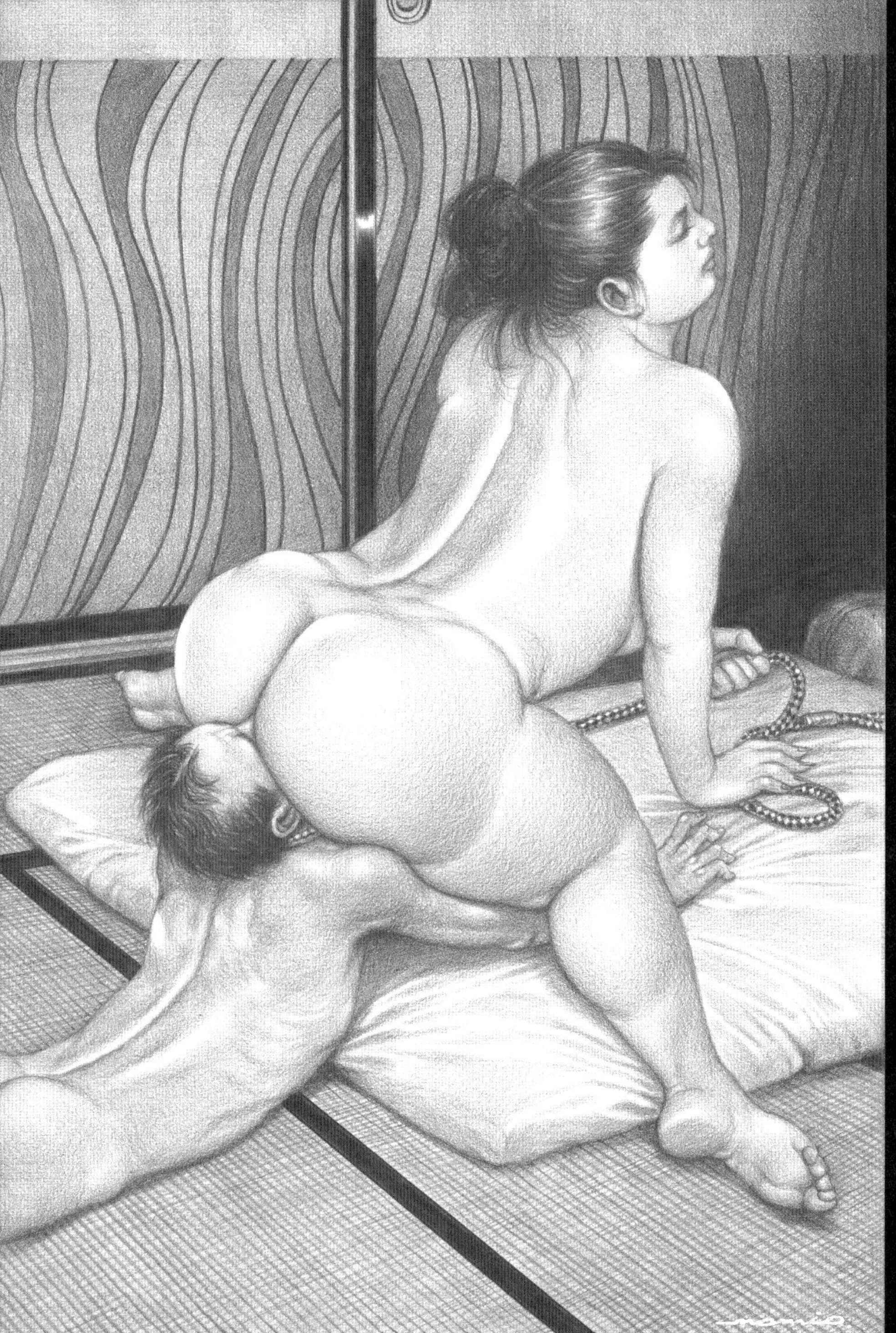

いつも通りにお茶のお稽古が始まった。和服姿の田丸美子が、燐として座っている。しかし、いつもと違うのは、艶やかなお尻の下に男が敷かれ、時々微かにうめき声が漏れる点である。
「先生、びっくりしました。お尻の下に男がいるなんて」
「敏ちゃんを驚かせたくて、レンタルを一日延長したのよ」
巨尻の下で浩がもがいた。
「すぐにもがくんだから……、静かになさい!!」
少しお尻を持ち上げ、空気を吸わせてやる。
「男をいじめるって楽しいわね。スッキリしたわ。敏ちゃんのおかげよ。ありがとう」
「でも、先生の大きなお尻に敷かれて、ちょっと気の毒ですわ」
「ホホホ、でもね、この男はいじめられたいのよ。いじめてあげているのよ。浩、口をお開け!!　食べさせてやるわ。いくわよ……そら」
「先生、すごいですね。私もレンタルします」

Tea practice began as usual. Wearing her kimono, Tamaru Yoshiko sat in a dignified pose. But, unlike other occasions, this time a man lay beneath her lustrous *oshiri*, and from time to time a faint moaning could be heard.
"Teacher, it's shocking to see that man beneath your *oshiri*."
"I wanted to surprise you so I extended the rental for a day."
Horoshi was writhing beneath Yoshiko's tremendous buttocks.
"You're always acting up. Be quiet, boy!"
Yoshiko raised her *oshiri* a bit to give Horoshi some air.
"It's just so much fun to abuse men. I feel refreshed. And, it's all thanks to you, Toshi-chan. Thank you."
"But I feel a bit sorry for him spread out under Teacher's very large *oshiri*."
"Ha, ha, ha! But this man wants to be abused. I'm doing him a favor. Horoshi! Open your mouth! I'll let you eat some. Alright, it's coming now."
"Teacher, I'm just amazed. I think I need to try renting one too."

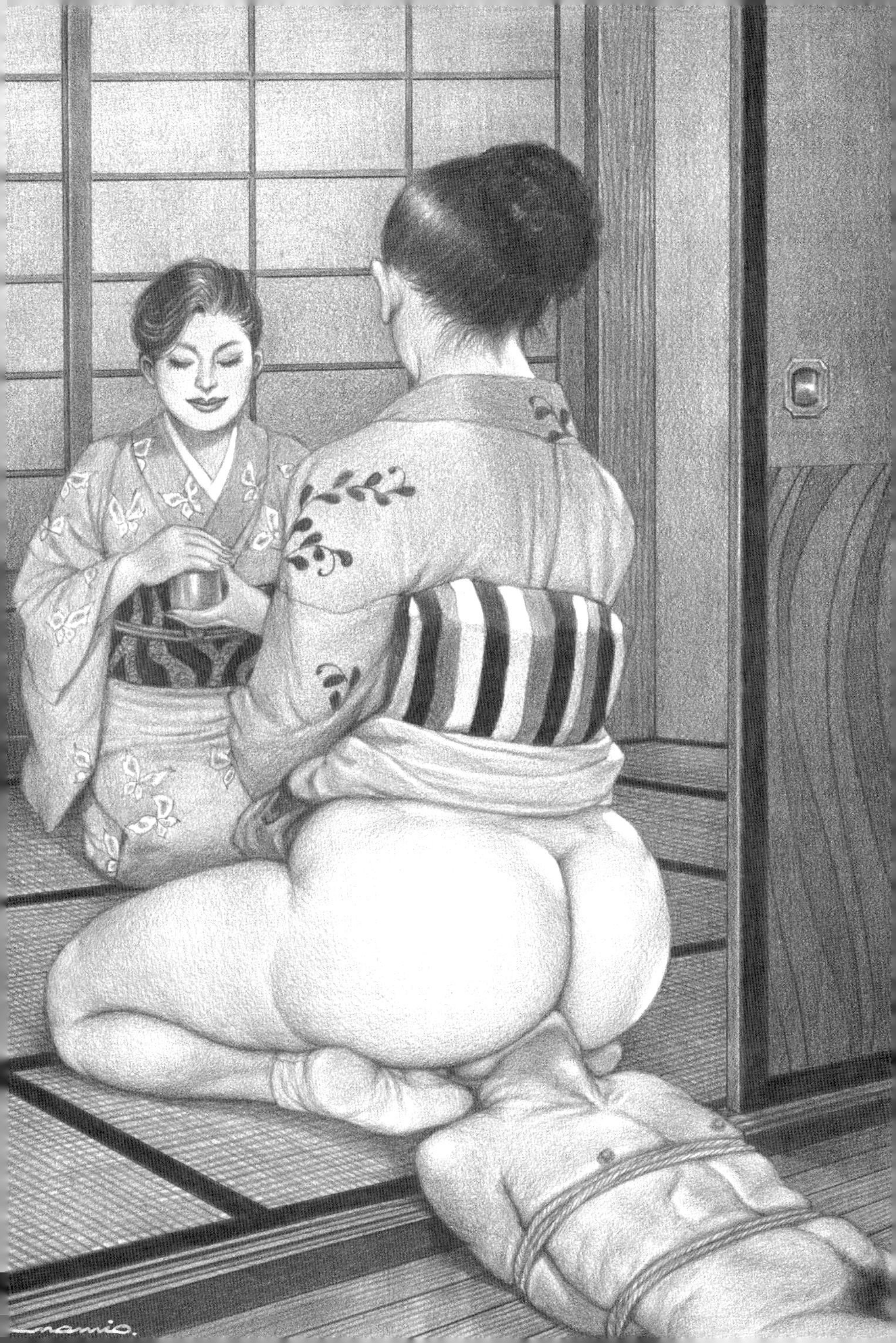
namio.

望むものは何でも与えられ、わがまま放題に育った社長令嬢・高岡裕子は、お嬢様高校の2年生。身長185cm、体重90kgの体格に加え、美人で勝ち気ときては、並の男には近寄りがたく、ひ弱な男たちにむしゃくしゃした裕子は、父親が出張で、お手伝いと二人きりになった時に、レンタル男を家に呼びつけた。
「ほら、しっかり歩きなさい!!　吾郎、本当にお前はノロマね。重いからって許さないわ、ほら、早く歩け!!　つぶれるまで降りないわよ」
裕子は、首輪のひもを引っ張り、吾郎にムチを入れる。
「お前は馬だろ、馬なら、しっかり歩け。ああ、いい気持ちになってきた、お前の背中が動くたびに、直接当たるのよ、あそこに。ほら、もっと、私をいい気分にさせるのよ」
ピシッ、ピシッ。ムチに打たれながら吾郎は必死で歩き続けたが、裕子の重さにつぶれ、動けなくなってしまった。

"The spoiled daughter of a company president, Takaoka Yuko was used to getting whatever she wanted. Now a sophomore at a preppy girls' high school, Yuko stood a tall 185 cm and weighed a very fine 90 kilos. Though she was not only beautiful but also strong-minded, Yuko had no time for typical boys. Instead, she found herself getting worked up over the weaklings. Yuko waited until her father was away on a business trip and she was left alone with the maid. It's then that she called in for a rental-man.
"Trot properly, I said. Goro, you really are lame. I'm not going to let you off easy, just because you say I'm heavy. Now get trotting! Quick! I'll ride you till you collapse." Yuko grabbed Goro's collar and applied the whip.
"You're a horse, aren't you? And if you are a horse, then you should trot. Ahh, that feels good. Whenever your back moves, it touches me right there. Come on, make me feel better."
Swisssshh. Swissshh. Goro did his best to trot while the whip rained down on him. Sure enough, Yuko's weight wore him down until he could no longer move.　　　　　　[185 cm=6'1" and 90 kg=198 lbs]

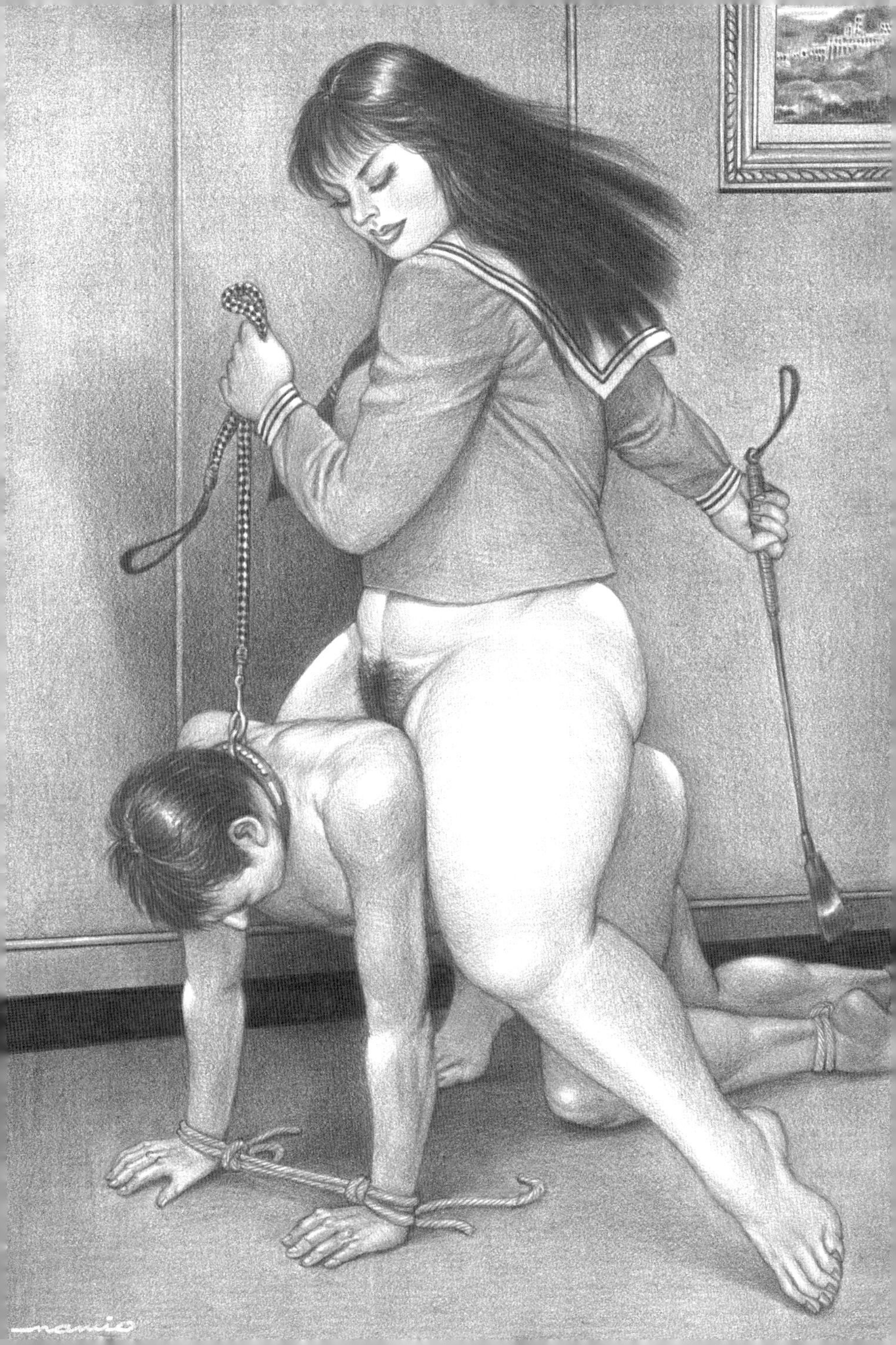
namio

90Kgの裕子を背にした人間馬・吾郎は部屋を2周したところでついえた。
「本当にだらしないわね、男のくせに」
裕子は足で吾郎を仰向けにすると、顔の上に腰を下ろし、もがき苦しむ吾郎の腕を足で押さえた。吾郎は足をバタつかせて抵抗するが裕子はピクともしなかった。
「動けば動くほど、顔がお尻に食い込んで苦しくなるわよ、ホホホ。ほら、もっと苦しめ」
その時、部屋の扉が開き、お手伝いの美樹がコーヒーを運んできた。
「お嬢様、その男は、どうしたんですか?」
「あら、美樹ちゃん、これはレンタルの奴隷なの。男をいじめるって、楽しいわね。でも、お父様には内緒よ」
「とても苦しそうにしてますよ……」
「そう、苦しむ男を見ていると感じるの。お尻から懸命さが伝わって、気持ちいいのよ。あら、動かなくなったわ、どうしたの?」
吾郎は巨尻の下で失神していた

Goro, the human horse, lasted only two trips around the room with Yuko's 90 kilos on his back before he collapsed.
"How lazy! And you call yourself a man."
Yuko used her foot to position Goro on his back, and then lowered her waist onto his head. She pinned the struggling Goro's arms to the floor with her feet. Goro resisted by thrashing his legs about, but Yuko didn't budge an inch. "The more you move, the more your face suffers. It gets smothered that much more by my *oshiri*. But, since you like to suffer, here goes …"
Just then, the door to the room opened and Miki, the maid, came in carrying some coffee.
"Young Miss, what is that man doing here?"
"Oh, Miki, this is a rental slave. It's so fun to abuse a man. But, please don't tell Father!"
"It looks like he's in a lot of pain."
"Yes, it feels so good to watch a man suffer. I can feel his determination through my *oshiri*, and that is so lovely. Oh, he's stopped moving. What could have happened?"
Goro had fainted under those massive buttocks.

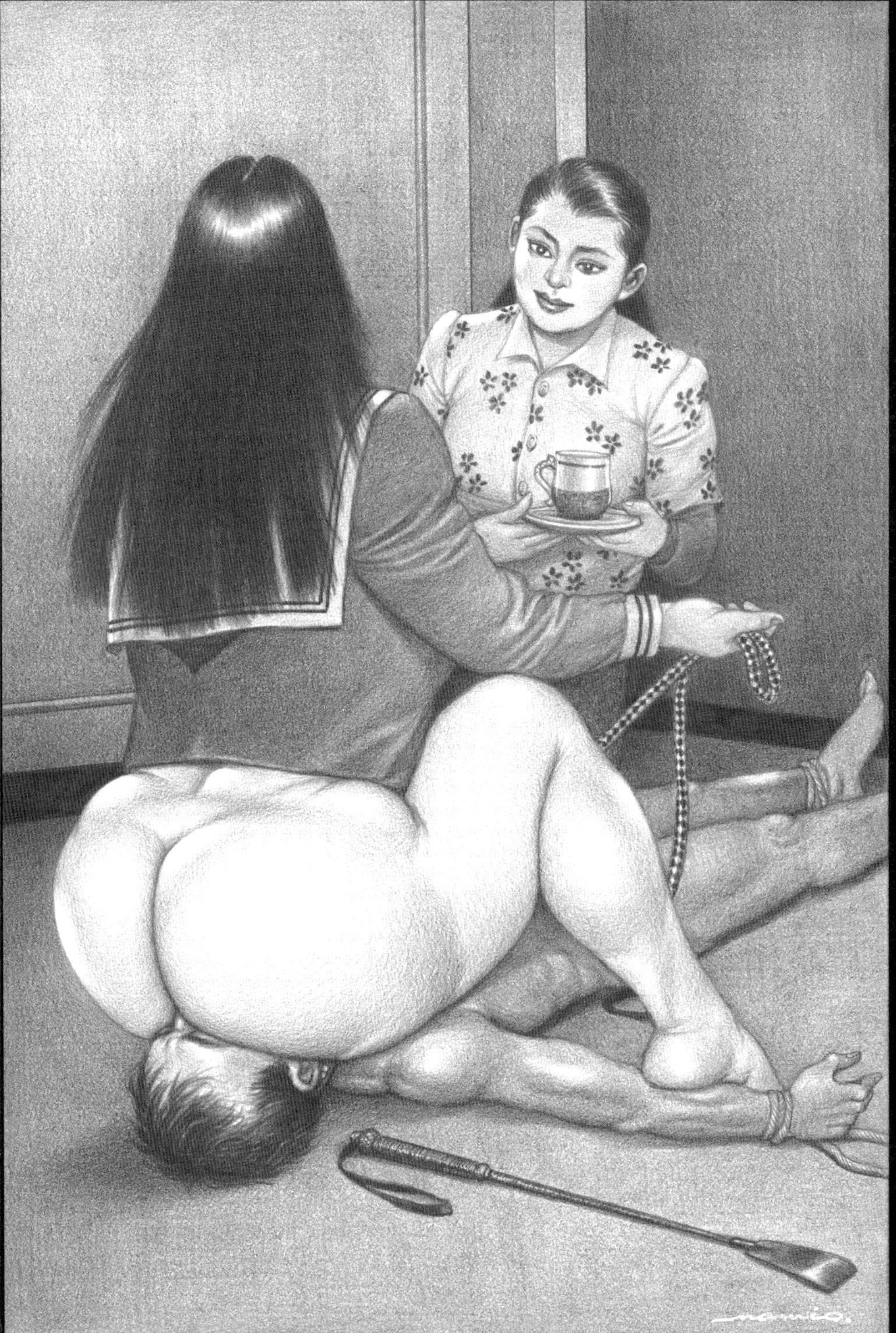

完璧に調教された吾郎も、裕子のヒップ責めにはあっけなく失神してしまった。
しかし、S性に目覚めた裕子はこれに飽き足らず、吾郎をリビングに引っ張ってゆき、ソファの前に座らせると、その前で大股を開いて座り、命じた。
「ほら、早く舐めろ。気持ちよくさせるのよ」
吾郎が股間に顔を埋め、繁みを掻き分け舌を懸命に動かすと、裕子はゆっくり足をあげ、徐々に吾郎の顔をお尻から飲み込んでいった。吾郎は迫るお尻を顔で受けながら、必死で穴の奥まで舌を動かした。
「ああ、お尻の中で舌がもがいている。吾郎の舌は最高よ。美樹ちゃんを呼んで、お前の惨めな姿を見せてあげるわ。美樹ちゃ〜ん」

Even Goro, who had received such perfect training, swooned quickly under Yuko's hip torture. But Yuko, who was just awakening to her sadistic nature, was not to be satisfied with this, and she pulled Goro into the living room. She ordered Goro to sit at the foot the sofa, and then opened her large thighs and sat before him.
"Hurry up and lick me. Make me feel good."
Goro buried his face in the crotch and diligently maneuvered his tongued through the growth. Yuko raised her leg slowly, and bit by bit used her *oshiri* to draw in Goro's face. Goro countenanced the advancing *oshiri* and frantically moved his tongue deep into the hole.
"I can feel your tongue struggling inside my *oshiri*. Goro, your tongue is exquisite. I'm going to call Miki, so that she can see what a pitiful sight you make… Miki!!"

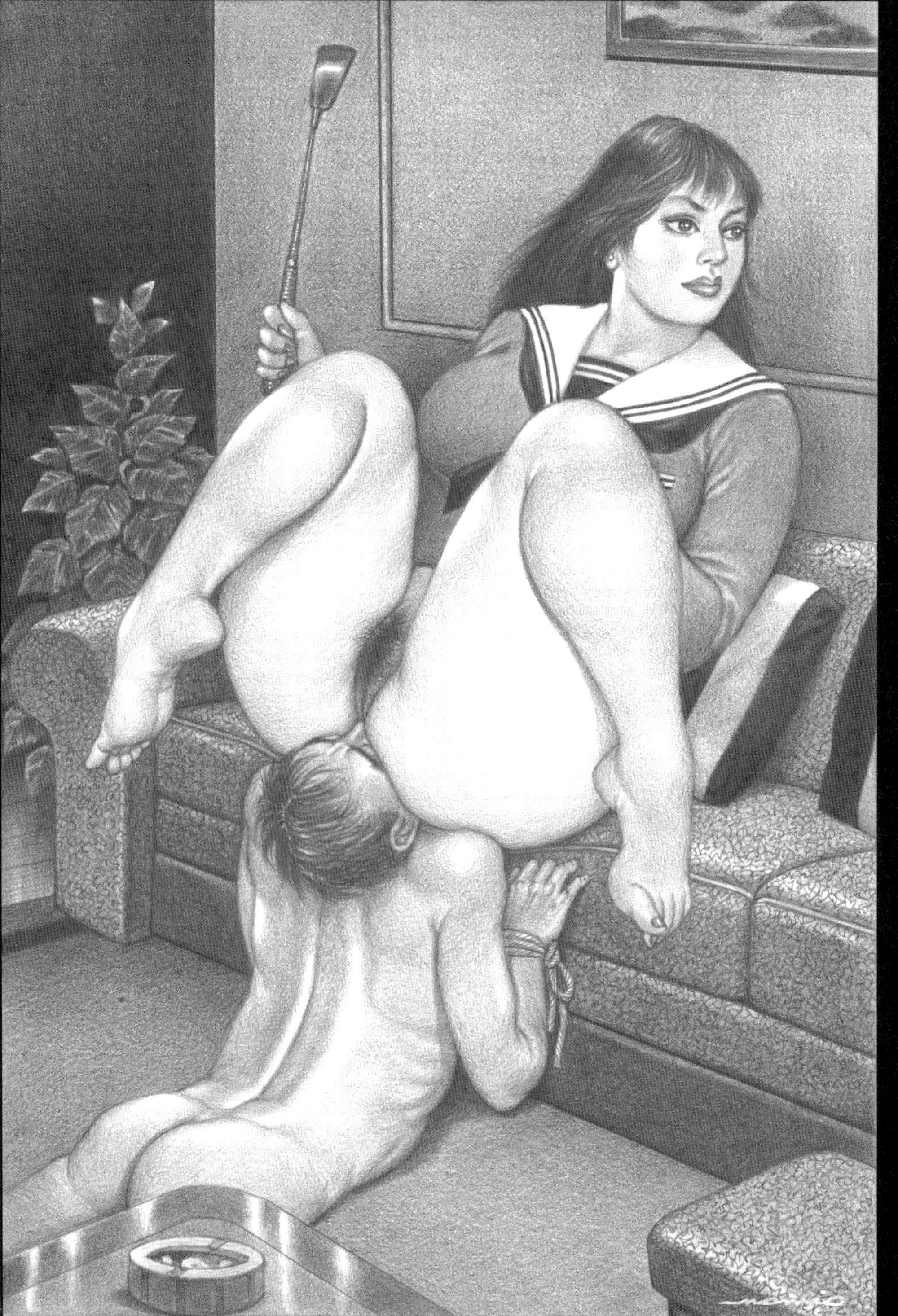

一晩中、ベッドで裕子の太腿に挟まれ舌奉仕を続けた吾郎は、翌朝、裕子の通学時間には、両手両足を縛られ、テラスで、裕子と美樹の足元に寝かされていた。
「よく頑張ったわね。気持ちよかったわ。私は学校に行くから、後は、美樹ちゃんに楽しんでもらうわ。美樹ちゃん、たのむわね」
美樹はタバコをくゆらせながら、吾郎の顔に豊満なお尻を落とした。
「ホホ、美樹ちゃんも十分Sのようね」
裕子は名残惜しげに学校に向かった。
「今から、お前は私の奴隷よ。こう見えて、私はお嬢さんより厳しいわよ。どこまでお前の舌が届くか、見せてもらおう。いいわね、もっと奥まで、そう……。オナラをするから口をお付け。ほら、〈ヴゥ〉、あ、すっきりした。つぎは、もっといいものをあげるわ。口に直接入れるのよ、全部食べるんだよ、さあ。出すよ、食べろ!!」

Goro serviced Yuko the whole night, pinned as he was between her thighs upon the bed. The next morning, just about the time when Yuko would leave for school, Goro—his arms and legs bound—was made to lie on the terrace at Yuko's and Miki's feet. "You did a good job. It felt very nice. I'm off to school now, so Miki-chan will be having fun with you. Miki, can you take over?"
Puffing at her cigarette, Miki dropped her rotund *oshiri* onto Goro's face.
"Miki-chan, you're quite the sadist too!" Yuko regretfully headed off to school.
"You're my slave now. Face it, I'm much stricter than the Miss. You'd better show me just how far that tongue can reach. Alright? Get in there deeper... yes. I'm going to fart now, so you just keep your mug right there. There we go." Miki gave a loud and heavy fart. "I feel much better. Now, I'll give you something much better. And I'll put it right into your mouth. You're to eat all of it, you hear? Okay, here it comes, so eat!"

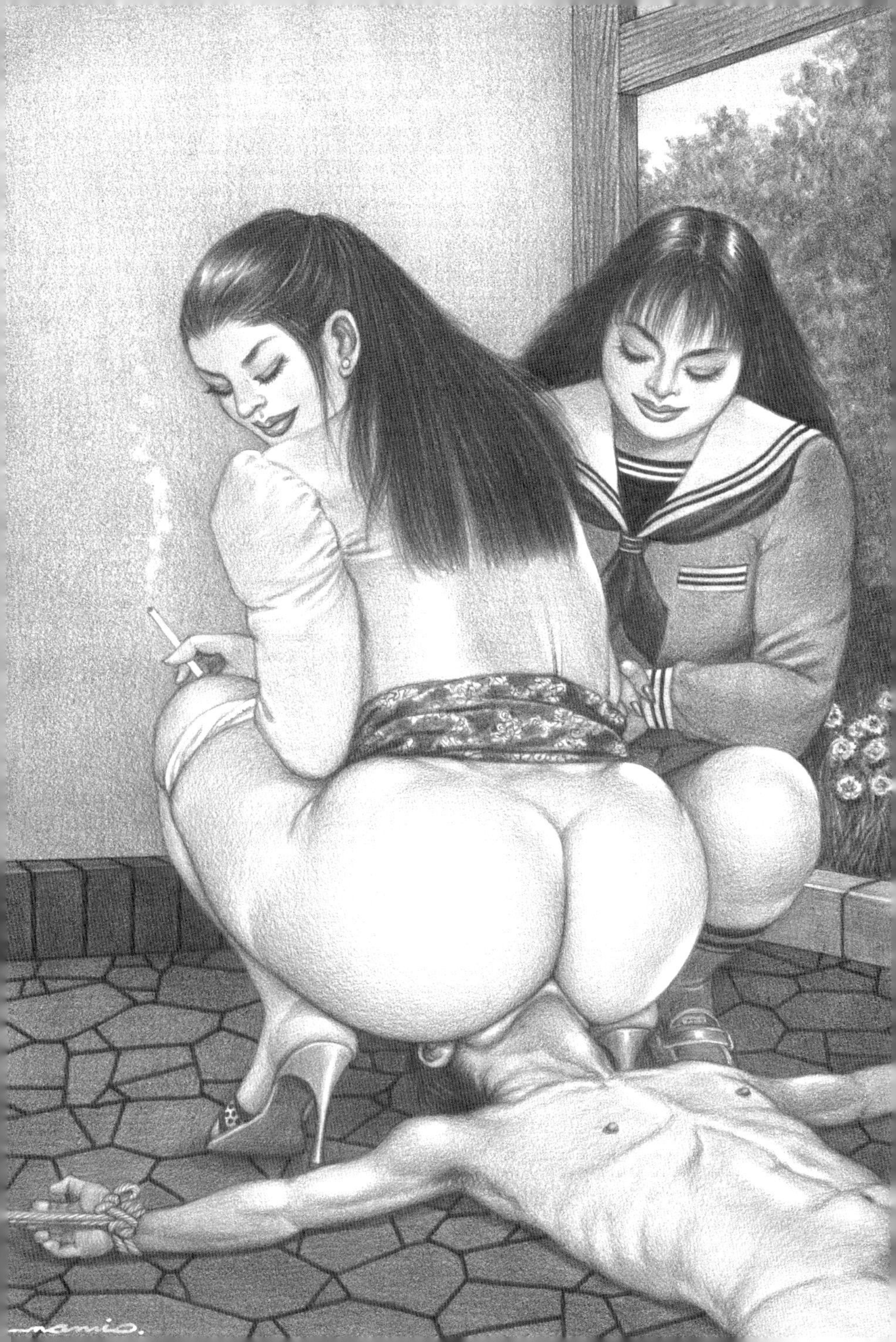
namio.

放課後、高岡裕子は、校舎の裏の約束の場所に急いだ。
「村田先生、お待たせ。私、すごい体験をしたの。それを知らせたくて。驚かないでね。先生はレンタル男って知っている？」
「レンタル男？」
「命令に絶対服従する男を借りられるの。それで思いっきりいじめてやったの。先生は離婚した後、男はもうコリゴリ、絶対忠実な奴隷みたいな男が欲しいって言っていたでしょう。その奴隷を連れて今晩、先生のお宅に伺います」
保健体育の教師・村田恵美と裕子は、何でも話ができる親しい間柄なのであった。
その晩、裕子を前に、恵美ははじめて130cmはあろう豊満な尻の下に男を敷いてみた。
「かわいそうだけど、男をいじめてみたかったのよ。この大きなお尻の下で泣かせてあげるわ。覚悟なさい、フフフ」

As soon as classes had finished for the day, Yuko Takaoka hurried to the agreed place behind the school. "Mrs. Murata, I'm sorry for making you wait. I had an incredible thing happen, and I just had to tell you as soon as I could. Don't be shocked. But have you heard of rental-men?"
"Rental-men?"
"You can rent a man who will completely obey your orders. And it's alright to abuse them as much as you want. Since your divorce, I know you've been fed up with men. And you even said you wished you had a man as faithful as a slave, didn't you? Well, I want to bring a slave over to your place tonight, Mrs. Murata."
The health and P.E. teacher, Murata Emi was on very intimate terms with Yuko. The two could share anything with each other. That evening, with Yuko as a witness, Emi tried for the very first time putting a man beneath her massive *oshiri*, one that boasted a girth around 130 cm.
"I feel sorry for you, but I really have been wanting to abuse a man. Just be prepared to shed some tears under my very large *oshiri*."  [130 cm = 51"]

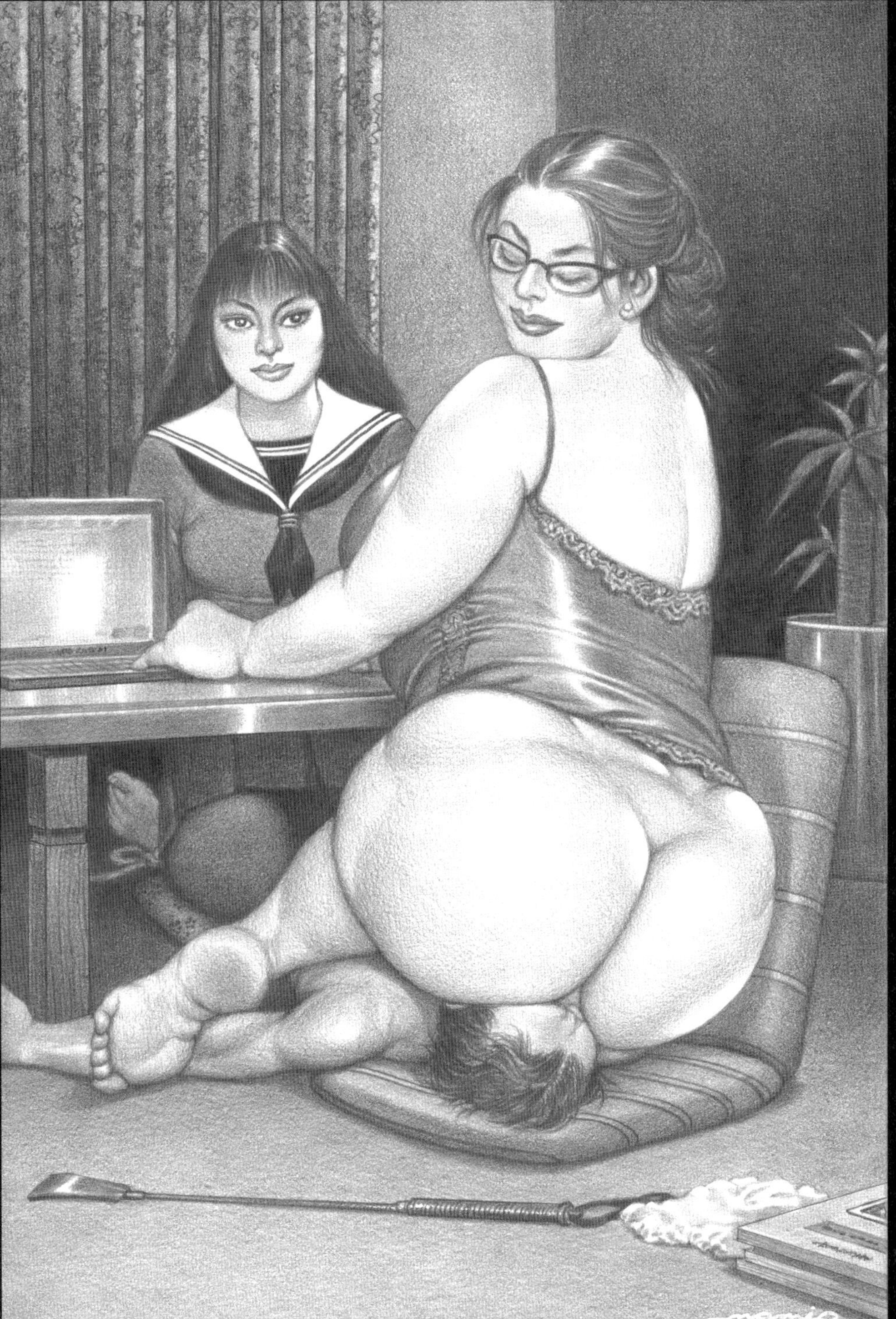
mamio.

半裸の恵美はリビングの椅子に男の両手を縛りつけると、テーブルの上にビールを並べ、大股を開いて男の前に座った。盛り上がった秘部と繁みが男の顔を包み込み、男が動くたびに埋もれてゆく。
「お前の名前は何ていうの?」
「は、はい、明男と申します」
「明男、私は色んな男を知っているけど、どいつもわがままで、勝手な動物よ。だからいつか男を泣かせてやろうと思っていたの。わかった? お前は私の忠実な奴隷よ」
酔いもまわり、恵美はテーブルに片足を乗せ、さらに明男を秘部にくわえ込んでゆく。
「明男、しっかり舐めろ。お前は犬だよ。ああ、最高、出そう、お前は命令に絶対服従すると言ったわね。出すわよ、いい、さあ飲め!! ブタ」
明男は噴き出す激流に必死で喉を鳴らした。

Half undressed, Emi tied the man's two arms to a chair, put a bottle of beer on the table, and sat down with her large thighs wide open before him. Every time he moved, the man sunk deeper, his face wrapped by her pubic growth and her fleshy pudenda.
"What's your name, boy?"
"Mi..Mistress. It's Akio."
"Akio, I've known many a man, but they've all been selfish pigs. So I've been wanting to make a man cry for some time now. You get that? You are my faithful slave now."
The alcohol was having its effect, and Emi lifted a leg onto the table. Akio sunk even deeper into her privates.
"Akio, you have to lick properly. You're a dog. Ah, that is great. It's coming out. You said you'd obey me completely, right? It's coming, now. There, drink it, you pig!"
Akio's throat was purring at the spouting torrent.

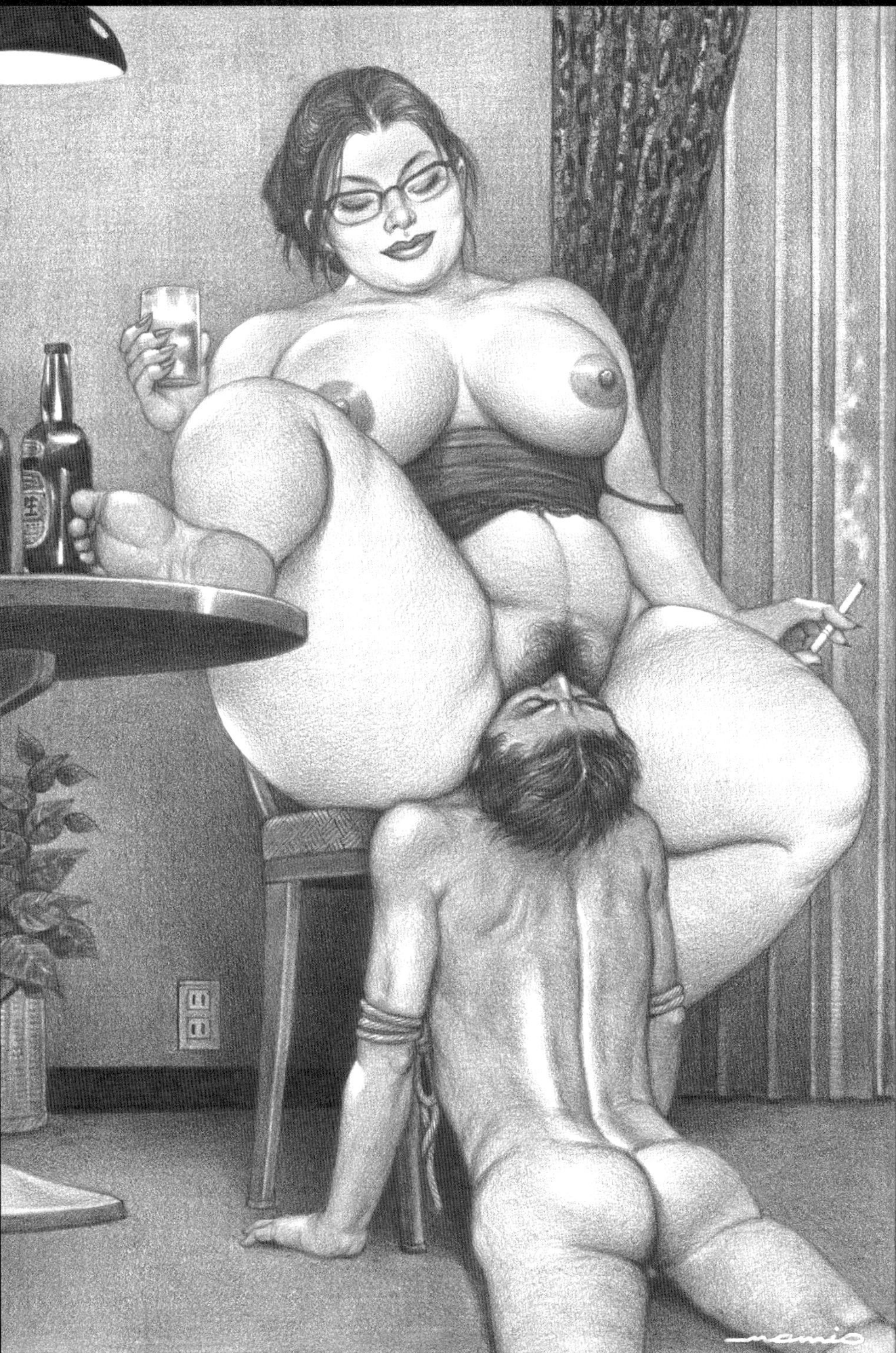

恵美は32才になるまで、人並みに男性を経験し、結婚後も普通の夫婦生活を送ってきたが何か満たされずにいた。恵美の体の上で自分が満足する為にセックスをする男たちに嫌悪感を覚えた。しかし、今は違う。男は恵美の股間で懸命に舌を動かしている。こんなに感じたことも初めてである。これこそが望んでいたセックスだった。酔いと絶え間ない舌の奉仕で何度もアクメに達し、恵美はソファに眠り込んだ。

目覚めても余韻が残る恵美は、全裸になり、明男に首輪をつけると、ひもを跨いでソファの肘掛けに腰を下ろし、思い切りそのひもを引いて、明男の顔をお尻の割れ目に引き寄せた。

「お尻の穴をしっかり、お舐め。どんな味がする?」

「はい、とっても美味しいです」

「よし、舌を入れてごらん。もっと美味しくなるわよ。そう、いいものをあげるわ、ほら、そのまま吸ってごらん。ああ、最高の優越感だわ」

Until she turned 32, Emi had had the usual sorts of experiences with men, and after her marriage too, she led a regular married life. But, all along, she felt that something was wanting. Indeed, Emi developed a hatred for men who had climbed upon her to satisfy their sexual needs. But, now was different. A man was diligently moving his tongue in her crotch; it was the first time for her to feel so good. This was the sex she had been dreaming of. Thanks to the alcohol and the ceaseless service of the tongue, she'd reached orgasm several times—and now she drifted into sleep upon the sofa.

Still feeling the ripples of her arousal, Emiko later awoke. She removed the last of her clothes and hooked a collar around Akio's neck. Straddling the rope attached to his collar, she lowered herself onto the sofa's armrest. She yanked hard on the rope and pulled Akio's face into the crack of her *oshiri*.

"Lick it well, boy. What's the taste?"

"It's so very delicious, Mistress."

"Good! Now put your tongue in. It's going to get even more delicious for you. Yes, I'm going to give you a treat. Keep sucking like that. Ahh, this makes me feel so superior!"

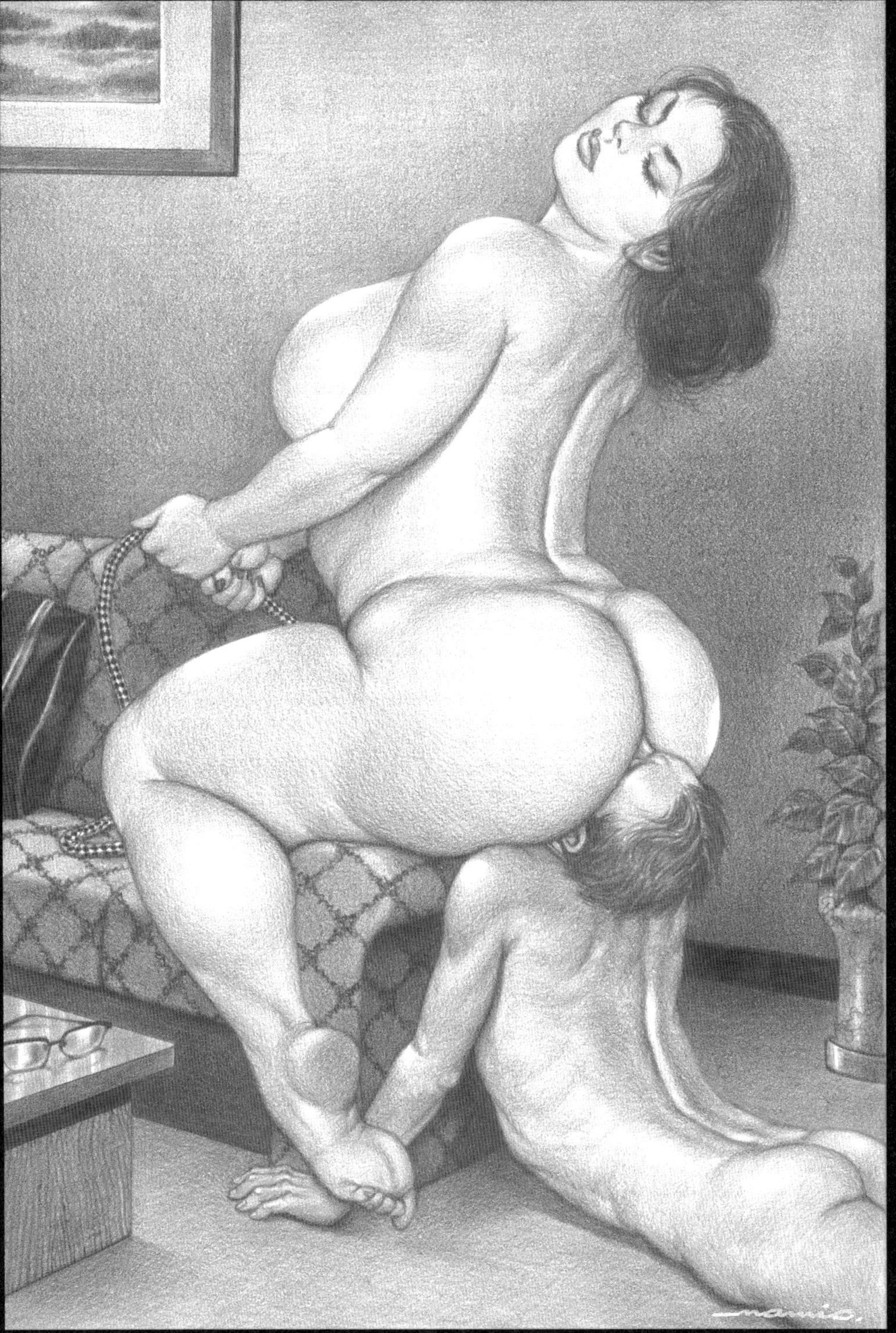

恵美にとって、命令に絶対服従の明男とのセックスは楽しすぎてとても眠れる状態ではない。明男をベッドに寝かせると、今度は縄で男根をしばりあげた。
「痛い？　我慢なさい。立派なローターがあるのだから、私には用がないのよ」
明男にローターをくわえさせると、顔に跨がり巨尻をゆっくりと下ろした。恵美は明男の顔を両手でおさえると、激しく腰を振った。
「よく頑張ったわね。でも、まだまだこれからよ。さあ、私のジュースをきれいに吸い取って」
ピシッ!!　恵美の乗馬ムチが飛んだ。
「しっかり吸い取らないから、シーツがビショビショじゃない。お尻の方まで舐めなきゃダメでしょう」
明男は、お尻の谷に沿って必死に舌を走らせる。
「気持ちいい、穴も舐めてちょうだい。中までよく舌を動かして、何かに当ったでしょう、ホホ、もうすぐ食べさせてあげるわ。でも、まだ、おあずけよ、ホホホ」

For Emi, so enthralled by sex with Akio, a man who would completely obey her every command, sleep was not a possibility. She forced Akio on the bed, and next began to tie up his cock.
"Does that hurt? Be patient, boy. I happen to have a very good vibrator but I've had no use for it."
She made Akio take the vibrator in his mouth, upon which she sat astride him, lowering her *oshiri* onto his face. Emi held his face with both hands, and began to passionately rock her tremendous buttocks. "You're doing fine! But, we've just started. Now I want you to swallow all my juice."
Crrackk! Emi's crop swung through the air. "You're spilling, and you've gotten the sheets all wet. I told you to lick all the way down to my *oshiri*."
Akio desperately ran his tongue along the *oshiri*'s valley. "That feels so good. Push your tongue deep inside. Did you feel something in there? Yes, I'll feed it to you soon. But, not yet! I'll keep it for you a bit more. Heh, heh, heh."

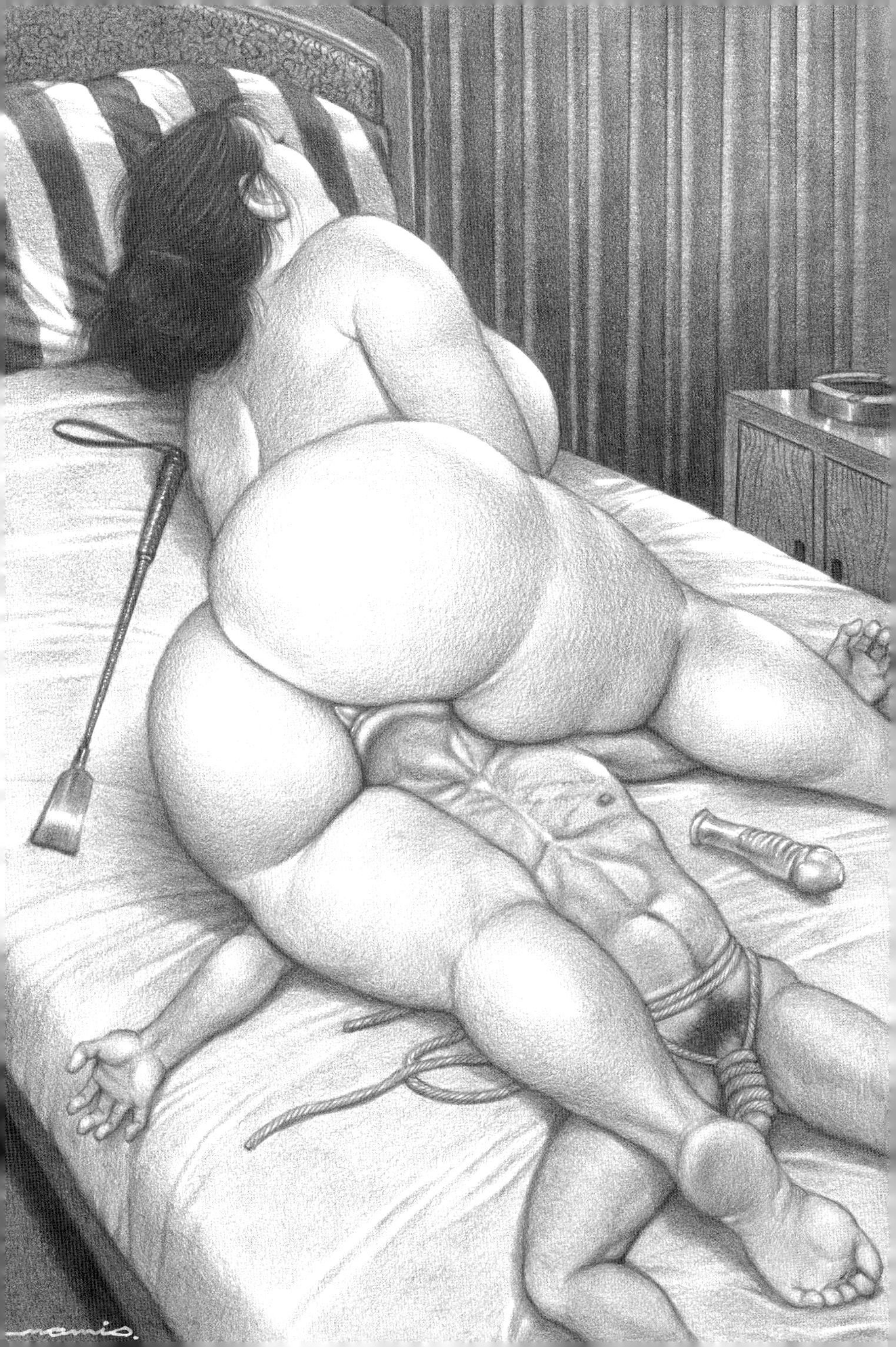
namio.

女性専用M男派遣業「女神たちのしもべ」のユーザーは急増し、大原加奈社長に憧れる男たちが挙って派遣社員に志願し、多様化する女性たちの要求に喜々として応えた。

タレントの小池栄湖はロケ中に足首を骨折、3ヶ月の入院生活を余儀なくされ、不自由な毎日に苛立っていた。

「トイレに行くのもたいへんだし、何とかならない？ そうだ、レンタル男を呼んでちょうだい。何でもしてくれるのでしょう」

婦長は栄湖のわがままに負けて、病院に内緒でレンタル男を呼び寄せた。

さて、男は部屋に入るなり驚きの声を上げた。

「小池栄湖様ですね。ありがとうございます。大ファンです」

男は小さく震えていた。

「そう、嬉しいわ。こっちにいらっしゃい。私は今、オシッコがしたいのよ、さあ、口をつけてお飲み。ほら出すわよ、こぼしたらダメよ、ああ、気持ちいい」

Minions to the Goddesses—the agency that supplied male masochists on short-term contracts for a female-only clientele—attracted a large following. The many men who'd fallen for President Kana volunteered en masse for the contract work, and they joyfully responded to their female clients' constantly diversifying needs.

Koike Eiko was a television celebrity who'd broken her ankle during some on-location shooting. There was no choice but for her to stay in the hospital for three months, and she grew irritated at being able to do so little. "What am I to do? It's hard for me even to use the toilet. I know! Get me a rental-man. I've heard they'll do anything."

The head nurse gave into Eiko's demand, and arranged for a rental-man to come discreetly to the hospital. When he entered the room, he exclaimed, "It's Mistress Koike Eiko! I am so honored. I'm such a big fan of yours." The man trembled nervously as he spoke.

"Yes, it's me, and I'm happy to hear that. Come over here, boy. I need to piss right now. So put your mouth there and drink. Okay, it's coming. You mustn't spill. Ahh, that feels so good."

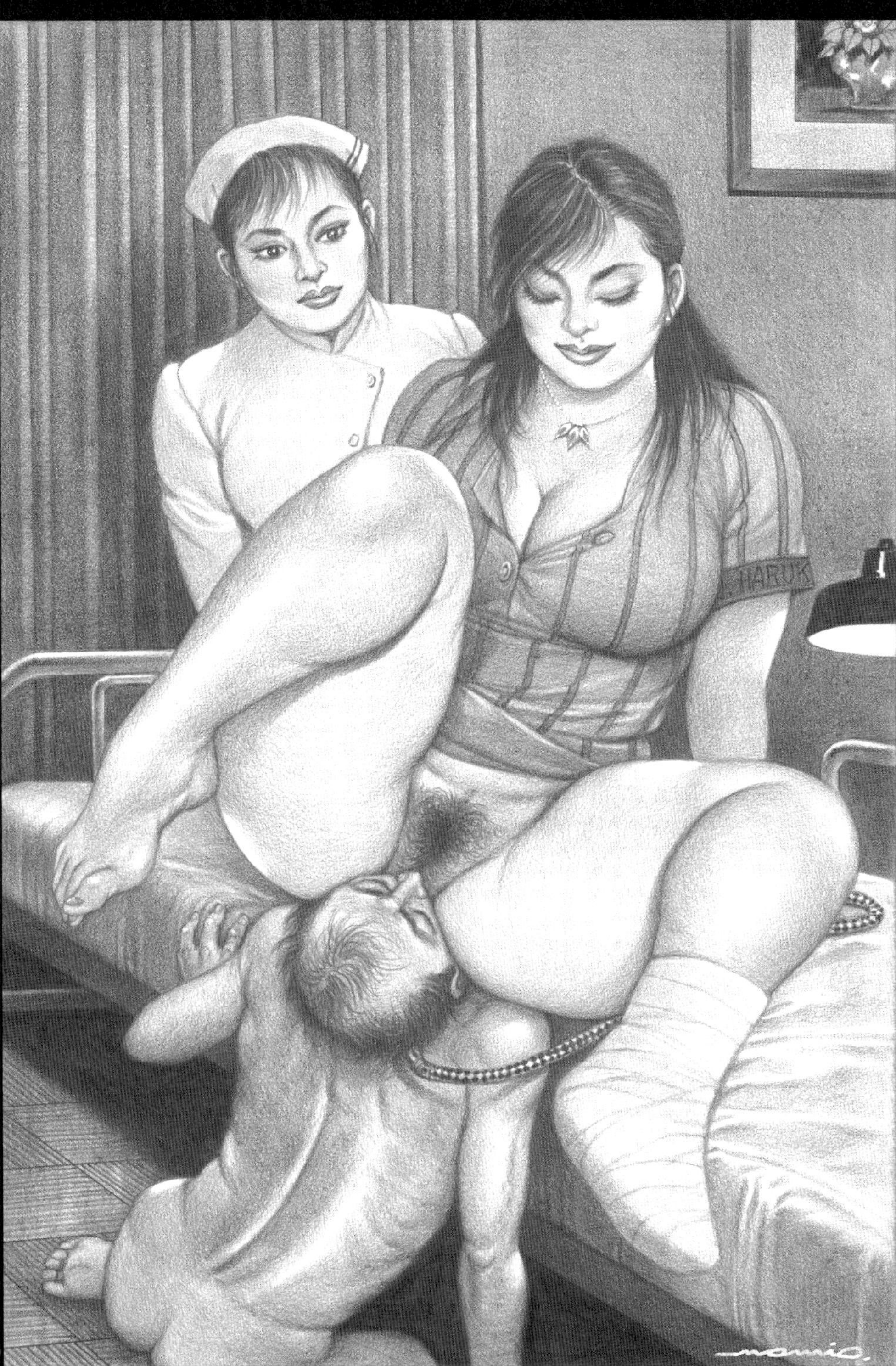
HARUK
namio.

レンタル男は、女性への崇拝度、奉仕テクニック、経験値などでA〜Dの4段階に格付けされる。栄湖に派遣された内田康は、どの点でも申し分ないA級で、人間便器としても優秀な能力を備えていた。
栄湖が目覚めると、ベッドの足元で待機していた康を呼びつける。
「康と言ったわね。ずいぶん頭の髪が薄いわね。いくつなの？ 55？ 父と同じだわ、妙な感じね。私のファンって、本当なの？」
「はい、光栄でございます。こんな幸福はございません。何でもご命令くださいませ」
栄湖はさっそく、首輪を引き寄せると、康の目の前にお尻を突き出し、卓越した人間便器の超舌技法を味わった。

The rental-men were grouped into four categories, A through D, according to their service technique, their experience, and the extent to which they worshipped their women superiors. Uchida Yasushi, who'd been provided to Koike Eiko, was a top-scoring Class A rental-man, and he was equipped with extraordinary skills as a human toilet.
"You said your name's Yasushi. You're getting pretty bald, aren't you? How old are you? Fifty-five? The same age as my father. Well, that feels a little weird. And you're really one of my fans?"
"Yes, I'm most honored to be so. Nothing could make me happier. Please order me however you wish."
Eiko wasted no time in pulling on his collar and sticking her *oshiri* right before Yasushi's eyes. She began to enjoy the superior tonguing technique of this distinguished human toilet.

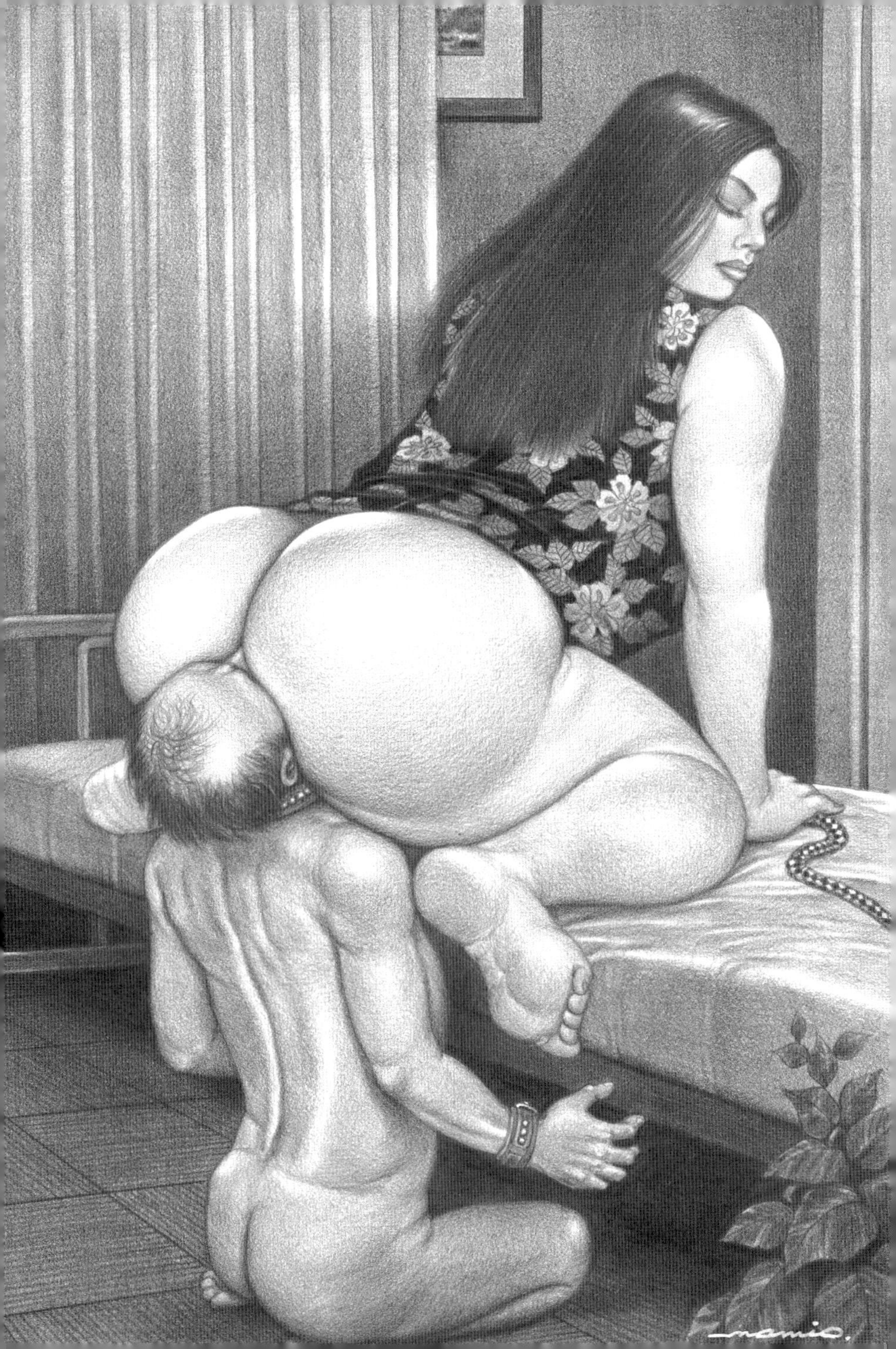

名前を呼べば、いつでも康がベッドの下から顔を出す入院生活は栄湖にとって楽しくて仕方がなかった。
「フフフ、私のお尻を舐められて嬉しい？」
「はい、便器にしていただけて幸福でございます」
「私のお尻はどう？　どんな味がするの？」
「はい、美しく輝き、口で言えないほどに香しく美味でございます」
「お前は、何も食べずに、今は私のウンチで生きているのね。いい気分よ。このまま、ずっと、お尻の穴に口を付けているといいわ、いつでも出来るものね。ああ、出るわ。さあ、お食べ」

Eiko began to thoroughly enjoy hospital life where, whenever she called his name, Yasushi would peer out from under the bed.
"Hmm... so you like being able to lick my *oshiri*?"
"Yes, Mistress, I'm overjoyed you've let me become your toilet."
"What do you think of my *oshiri*? What does it taste like?"
"It has a beautiful luster, but, I can't express in words how savory and delicious it is."
"You can survive without eating, survive just on my shit alone, right? It feels good. It'd be best if you can keep your mouth plastered—just like this—to my *oshiri*. Then I can go whenever I want to. Ahh, it's coming. Eat up, little man."

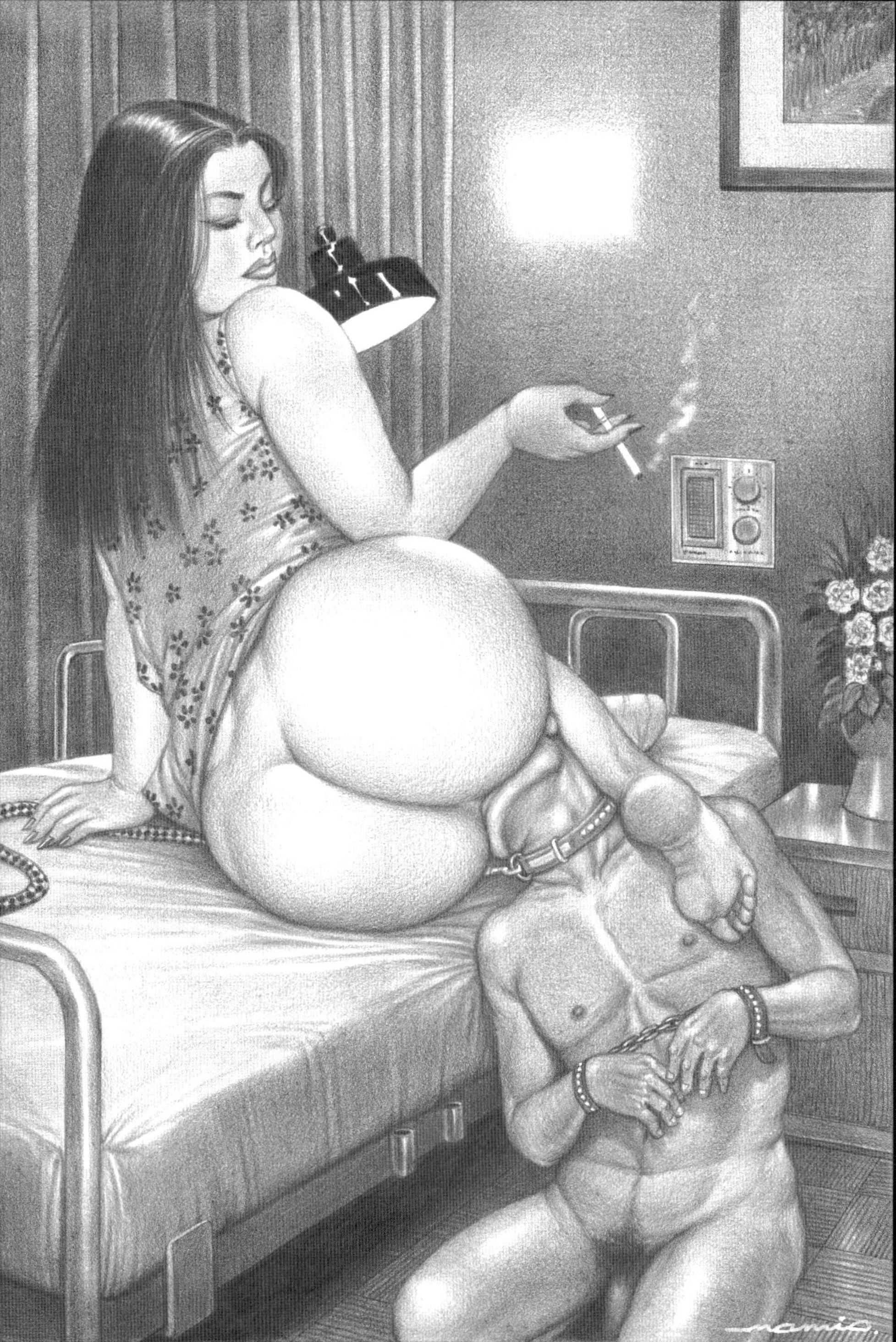

栄湖は康のレンタル期間を延長し、心ゆくまで人間便器を楽しんだ。
康をベッドに仰向けに寝かせ、その顔を覆い隠すほどの巨尻で腰掛け、コーヒーを啜りながら、康が苦しみ吸着する感触を味わった。十分に調教された康とて5分が限界である。失神寸前で、お尻が上げられる。
「ほら、お前の好きな小池栄湖のお尻をしっかり受けなさい。頑張らなきゃ、ダメよ。このまま、ウンチを食べさせてあげるからね。いい?」
強烈な重圧の中、死にもの狂いで康は飲み込んだ。
「最高よ、康、よく頑張ったわね」

Eiko extended the rental period and enjoyed her human toilet to her heart's content. Sometimes she would lay him facing upwards on the bed and sit so thoroughly upon Yasushi with her tremendous buttocks that his face would be completely covered. She would enjoy the feel of him struggling to suck her as she sipped her coffee. Very well trained though he was, Yasushi couldn't last more than five minutes. Just as he was about to faint, the *oshiri* would rise.
"It's your favorite… Koike Eiko's *oshiri*. So take it all in. Try harder! That's no good. Just like this… yes… I'll be giving you my shit to eat."
Under the oppressive burden, Yasushi swallowed down the shit as if his life depended on it.
"Very nice, Yasushi, what a good job!"

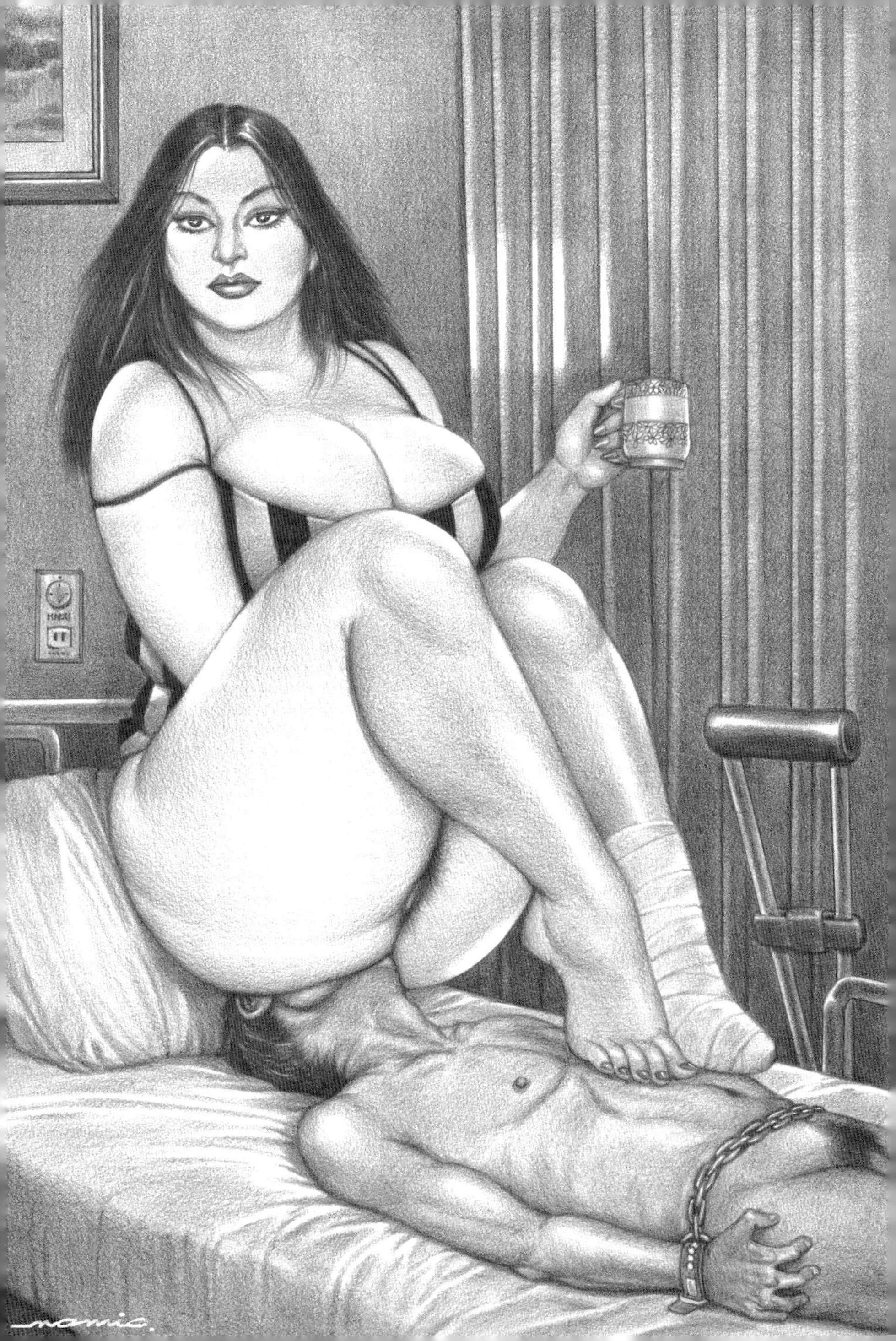

「女神たちのしもべ」は全国規模に拡大し、男たちの調教も一段と厳しさを増し、遂に完璧な人間便器が完成した。男たちは皆、美しいご婦人たちのお尻の下で奉仕できることに喜びを覚え、生き甲斐を感じていた。
加奈がプロデュースした婦人トイレに、デザイナーの山下小夜子がやって来た。
「あら、本当に男が待っているのね。立ったままオシッコをするなんて、変な気分ね」
固定された男の前で、パンティを下ろすと、局部を口の手前に持っていってやる。男は見事な繁みをかきわけ、口を大きく開け、待ち受ける。遠慮がちに走り出た流れは、やがて強烈な勢いとなり、男の口を襲い、胃袋へと飲み下された。その後、男は舌を伸ばし、繁みのしずくを吸い取り、後始末をする。
「あら、丁寧なこと。ありがとう。10分1000円でこんなに爽快になれるのなら、また来るわ」
小夜子はパンティをあげると、何事もなかったかのように、涼しい顔で街に戻って行った。

Minions to the Goddesses expanded into a national operation, and the men's training grew that much stricter. Finally, the perfect human toilet was developed. All the men felt such joy at being able service their ladies' *oshiri*; they had finally found what made life meaningful.
Yamashita Sayoko, a designer, approached the Ladies Toilet that Kana had invented.
"There's really a man waiting in there! It sure is a strange feeling to piss while standing."
This is how it is done: First you lower your panties in front of the man secured to the spot. Then put your privates right in front of his mouth. The man will make his way through your luscious growth, open his mouth wide, and wait. Your flow, perhaps nervously modest at first, will grow in force, and overcome the man, who will take it all the way down his gullet. After that, the man extends his tongue, and wipes the droplets from your thicket and tidies you up.
"That's so very clean. Thank you. If I can feel so refreshed in ten minutes and for only a thousand yen, then I'm sure to come back."
Sayoko raised her panties, and with a cool look, as if nothing had happened, she returned to the bustling town.

*Japan's Very First Ladies' Only Human Toilet. Have a blast—standing up!!*

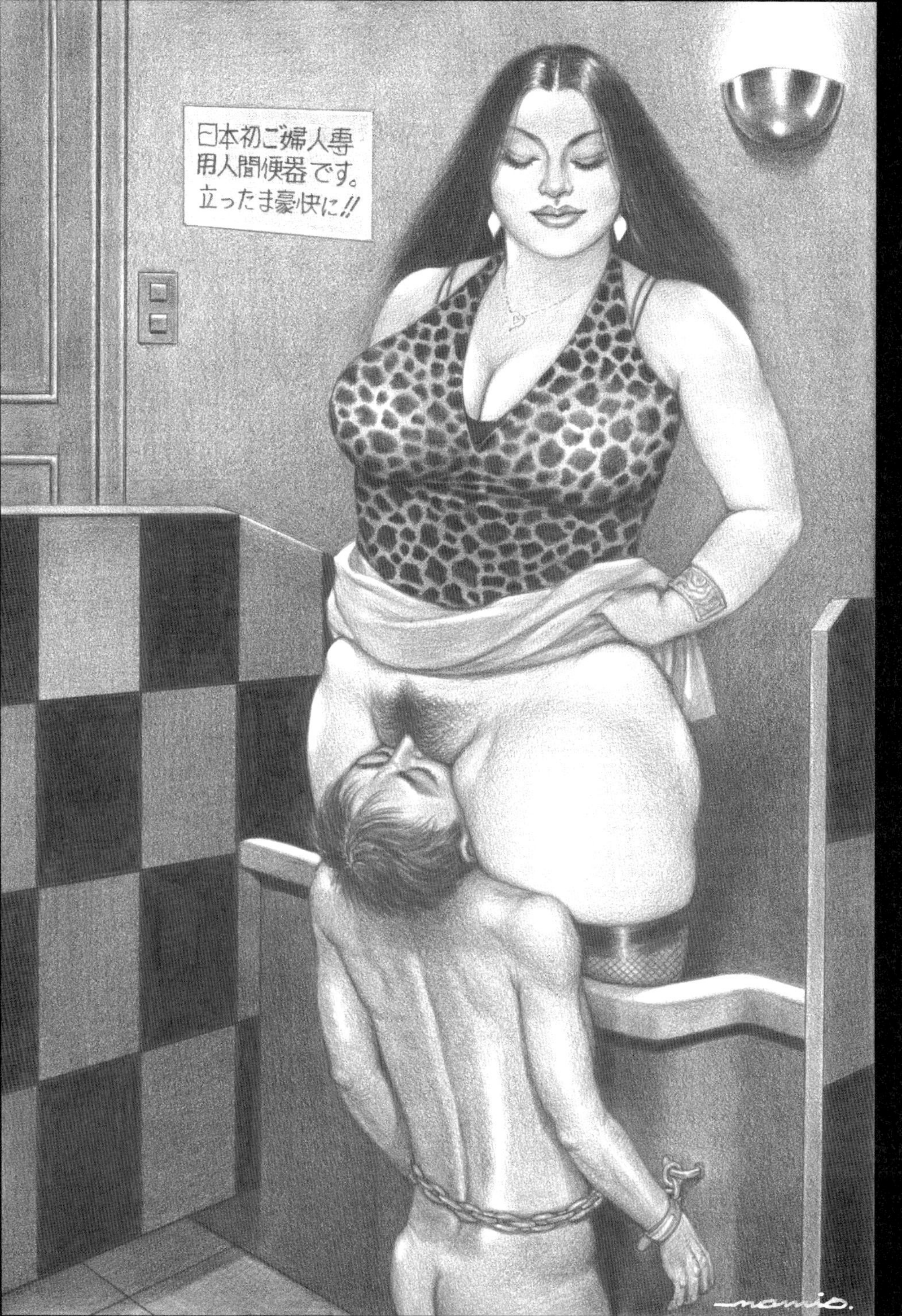
日本初ご婦人専
用人間便器です。
立ったま豪快に!!

立位の便座に続いて、腰掛け便器も繁華街の一角に設置され、話題をさらった。
利用料金は15分2000円と高額だが、早く体験したいという女性たちが列を作った。一番乗りのホステス、マリが便座に話しかける。
「すごいわね。どっちを向いて座ればいいの?」
「お嬢様が黄金を下さる場合は、私の方にお尻をお向けください」
「黄金を下さるなんて言葉、気に入ったわ。本当に、私の黄金を全部、食べられる? フフフ」
マリがスカートを捲りあげ、便座にどっかり座ると、男はお尻に顔を埋め、ゆっくり舌でアナルを刺激した。
「あ、出る。ああ、いい……。全部食べたのね。スッキリしたわ」
アヌスを舌で始末する男にマリが訊く。
「私のウンチの味はどうだったかしら」
「たいへん美味しゅうございました。ありがとうございます」

Following upon the success of the urinal, a sitting toilet was set up in a corner of the downtown. Soon the talk of the town, the facility was not a cheap one, at 2000 yen for fifteen minutes. But it didn't take long for a line to form of women eager to try it for themselves. Mari, a bar hostess who had been first in the queue, spoke to the toilet.

"This is amazing. But which way should I be facing sitting down?"

"If the Lady is giving gold, then please position your *oshiri* towards me."

"Giving gold—I like the sound of that. But can you really eat all the gold I've got to give? Ha! Ha! Ha!"

Mari pulled her skirt up, and settled onto the toilet seat. The man promptly buried his face in her *oshiri* and slowly stimulated her anal orifice with his tongue.

"Oh, it's coming. Ahh! Yeee! You've eaten all of it. And I do feel much better." Mari enquired of the man who was cleaning her anus with his tongue. "I wonder how my shit tasted?"

"Thank you very much, M'lady. It was most delectable."

*It's thrilling! It's refreshing! It's your Human Toilet!*

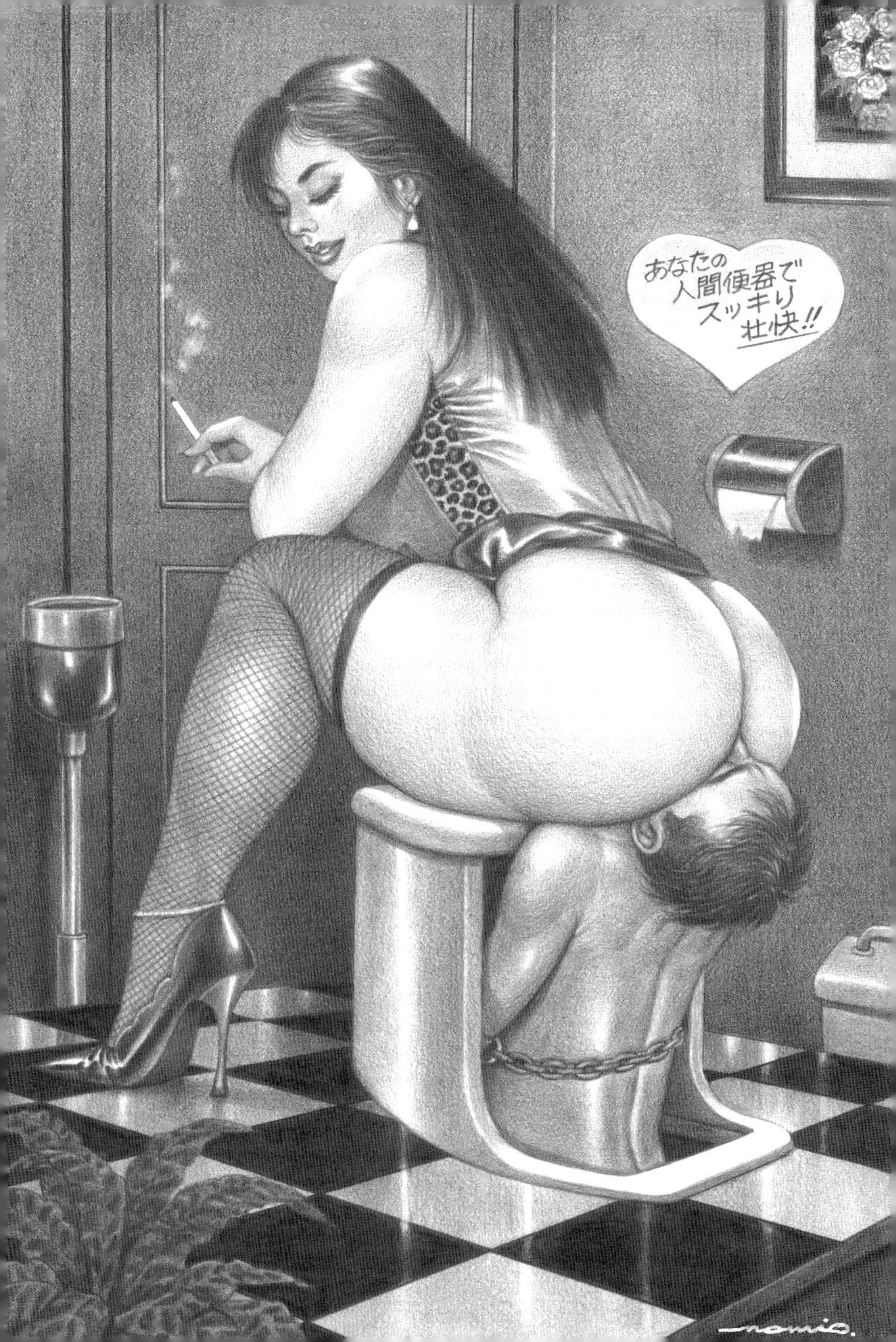
あなたの
人間便器で
スッキリ
壮快!!

前代未聞の人間便器は、利用希望者に整理券を配布するほど盛況を極めた。絶え間ない利用は人間便器の処理能力の限界を超えた。そこで、5人の男が交代で便器を務め、後始末係2名も追加されることになった。
大柄なOL高木洋子は飲み会帰りにトイレに立ち寄った。
「あ〜、飲み過ぎて、ウンチが出そうなのよ。でも男の口にウンチをするなんて考えられないのよね。本当に食べられるのかしら」
すると、男の口が洋子のアナルにピタリと吸い付き、ユルユルと排泄される黄金を飲み込んだ。
「ああ、出る、出る。気持ちいい。後は始末をしてちょうだい」
便器男と交代に後始末男が穴から顔を出す。
「あら、あなたが清めてくれるの。まぁ、中まで!? よく吸って、もっと！　もっと吸うのよ」

This unprecedented human toilet became so popular that tickets needed to be distributed to give some order to the waiting crowds. But still it was impossible for the human toilet to dispose of all the waste from such a never-ending line of users. It was decided that five men were to take turns as toilet, while two more were to be responsible for the tidying afterwards.
A big-boned office worker, Takagi Yoko made a stop by the toilet on her way home from a night out drinking. "Darn, I've had too much to drink, and I think I have to shit as well. But, I'm not really the kind of woman who dreams of shitting in a man's mouth. I wonder if they can really even handle eating it?"
Just as she uttered those words, the man's mouth perfectly attached itself to Yoko's anus, and began to drink down the watery gold that was being expended. "Oh, it's coming, it's coming out. This feels so good. Now, please clean me up, boy."
The tidy-man took over from the toilet-man and stuck his face in the opening. "You'll be my cleaner? Well, then, I want you to go all the way in. Suck it out… More! Didn't I tell you to suck!"

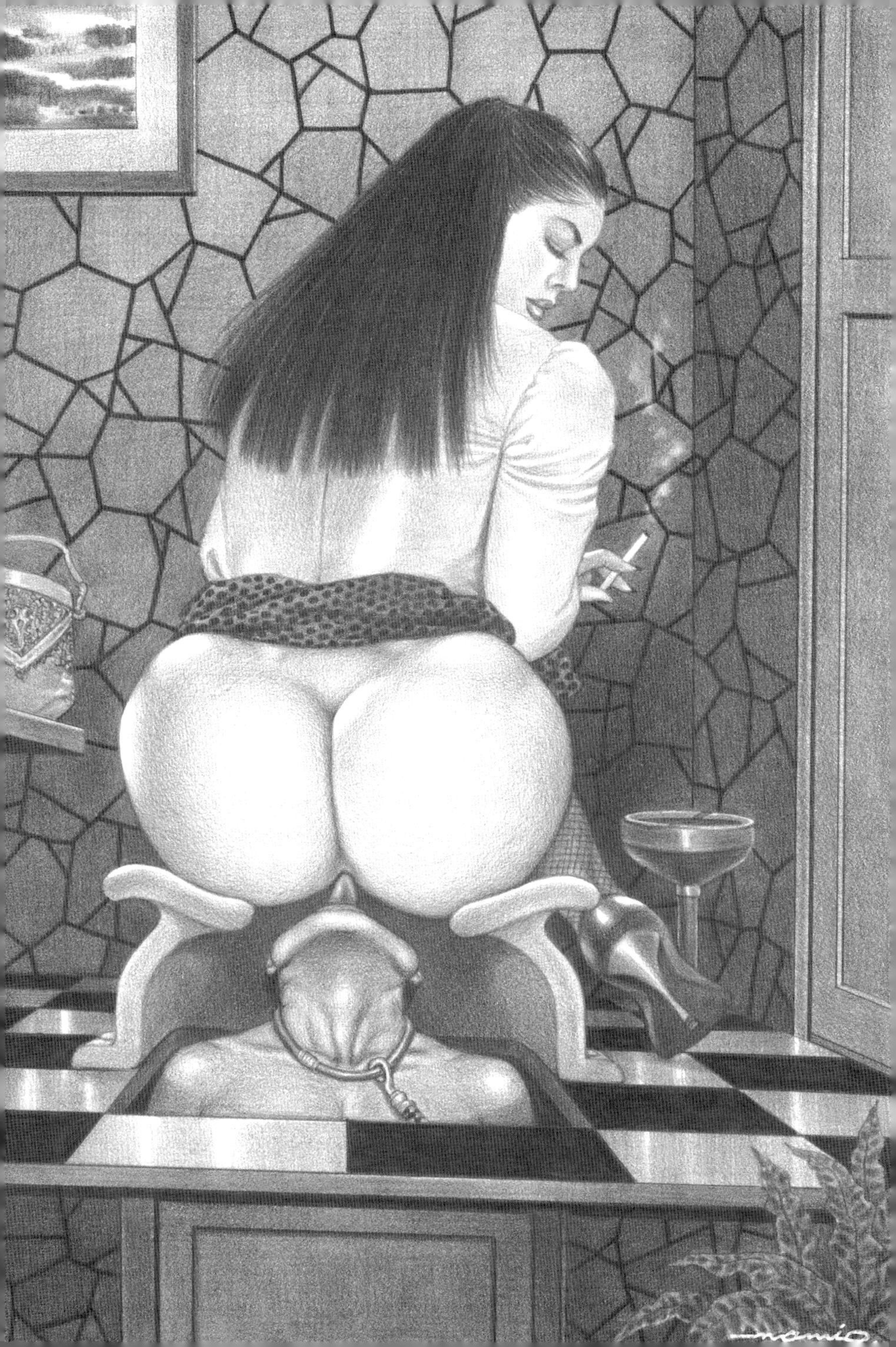
manio.

一日に何度も人間便器を利用する愛用者に向け、さらに優雅でゆったりしたトイレタイムを提供する特別人間便器室が開発された。
おしゃれな便座でコーヒーを飲みながら舌奉仕が楽しめるとあって、ストレスの多いOLたちが足繁く通うようになった。
OL土井信子は、便座に腰を下し、コーヒーを注文する。
「あ〜、あのバカ課長ときたら、頭にくる。さあ、お尻を舐めて気持ちよくさせてちょうだい。それにしても、あなたは、お尻を舐めてウンチを食べさせられて悲しくはないの?」
舌を休めずに、男は答える。
「いいえ。とても幸福を感じております」
「まあ、本当に嬉しいのね。不思議だわ。でも、これも現実なのよね」
信子は男の口にオナラを放っては無邪気に笑い、最後に極太の長いウンチをひねり出した。
「ホホホ、目を白黒させて、楽しい、ホホホ」

Targeting aficionados who preferred using the human-toilet more than once a day, the organizers developed Executive Human-Toilet Facilities that could provide a more elegant and restful toilet-time. Stressed-out female office workers began to pay regular visits to receive tongue service, perched on particularly stylish toilets while sipping at their coffee.
One these office workers, Inoue Nobuko, sat herself down on the toilet and ordered her coffee. "Oh, that asshole boss I have just pisses me off. So, boy, I need you to lick my *oshiri* and soothe my nerves. Don't you ever get down having to kiss ass and take shit all day?"
The man replied, never once resting his tongue.
"No, M'Lady. This is great joy for me."
"So you're actually are happy when you do that? Seems weird to me. To each man his own, I guess." Nobuko farted into his mouth and laughed innocently. Then she squeezed out a massively long and bulbous shit. "But it's sure fun to make your eyes spin. Tee-hee-hee."

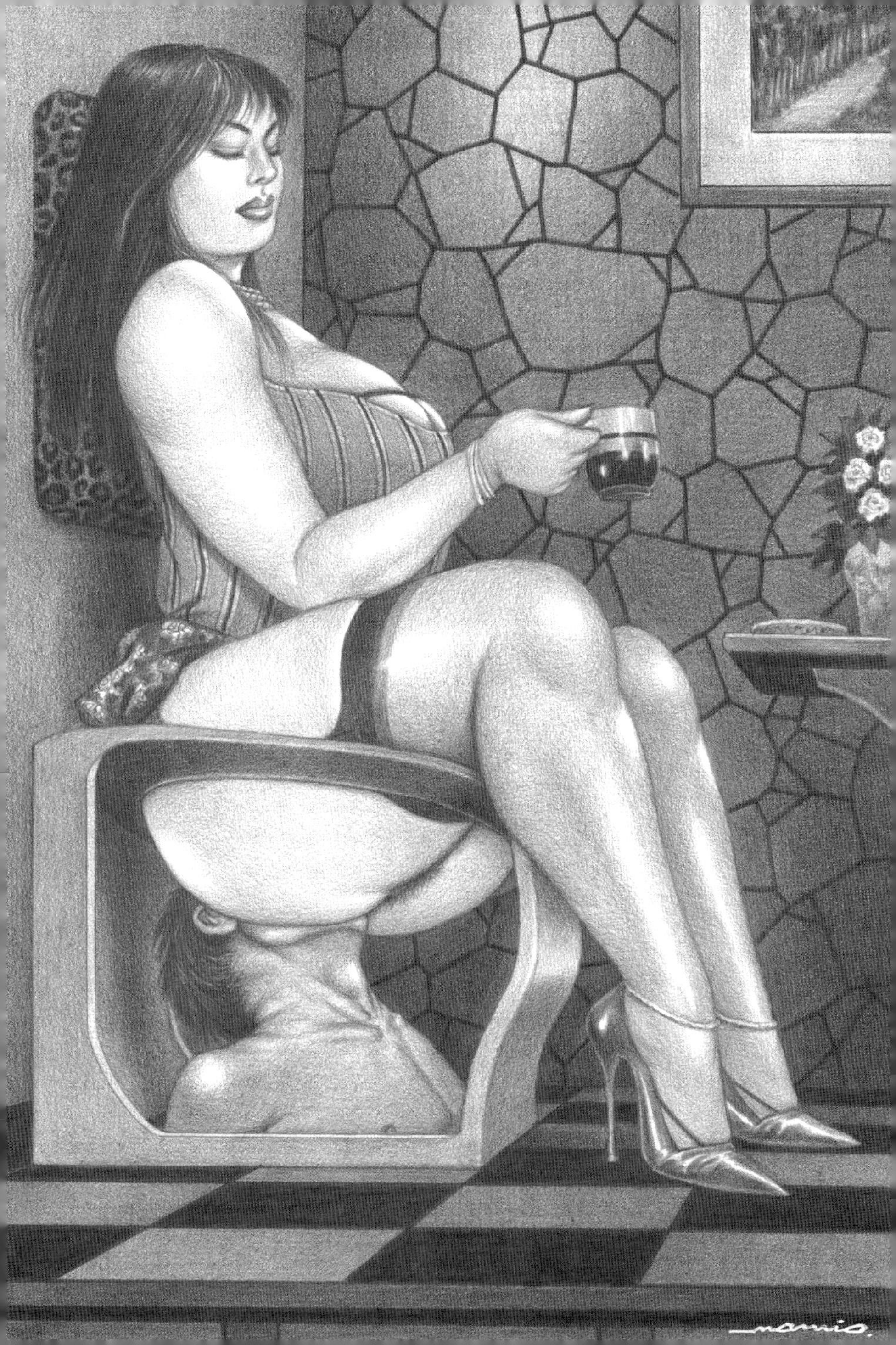
namio.

化粧品会社の社長に就任し、経営手腕を発揮し、次々に新事業を成功させ、女性の地位と美しさを向上させた加奈は、男たちの崇拝の対象であり、女性たちの憧れの的であった。

加奈の噂は海外にも広まり、日本の忠実な男を試したいと、アメリカから金髪の巨女が来日した。加奈がバレーボールの選手時代から交流のある、元アメリカ代表のキャメロンである。

食事に招待した加奈は久しぶりにキャメロンを見て驚いた。2mを超える長身のアタッカーは、現役時代の2倍はあろう体重140kgに達していた。

さっそく、キャメロンが宿泊する高級ホテルのスイートルームに二人の男が派遣された。キャメロンは、巨大なヒップに男の顔を挟み込み、苦しむ男の姿に笑みを浮かべた。

Having taken over as president of a cosmetics company, shown her skills as a manager, and demonstrated her ability to bring success to one business enterprise after another, Kana had improved both women's social standing and their beauty in the world. It was little surprise she would become an object of worship for men and of admiration for women.

Word of Kana spread overseas, and one day a blonde giant arrived from the States, saying that she wanted to try for herself Japan's faithful men. Of course, Kana had known Cameron, since her volleyball days when Cameron had been on the US national team.

Kana had invited Cameron invited for dinner, but she was astounded at what she saw. The former setter, who stood over 2 meters tall, must have doubled her weight since her time on the team. It looked like she would now weigh in at about 140 kilos.

No time was wasted in dispatching two men to the luxury hotel suite where Cameron was staying. Cameron pinned the two men down with her massive hips, squashing their faces and growing more and more delighted at the sight of their suffering.

[2 meters = 6'6" / 140 kg = 308 lbs]

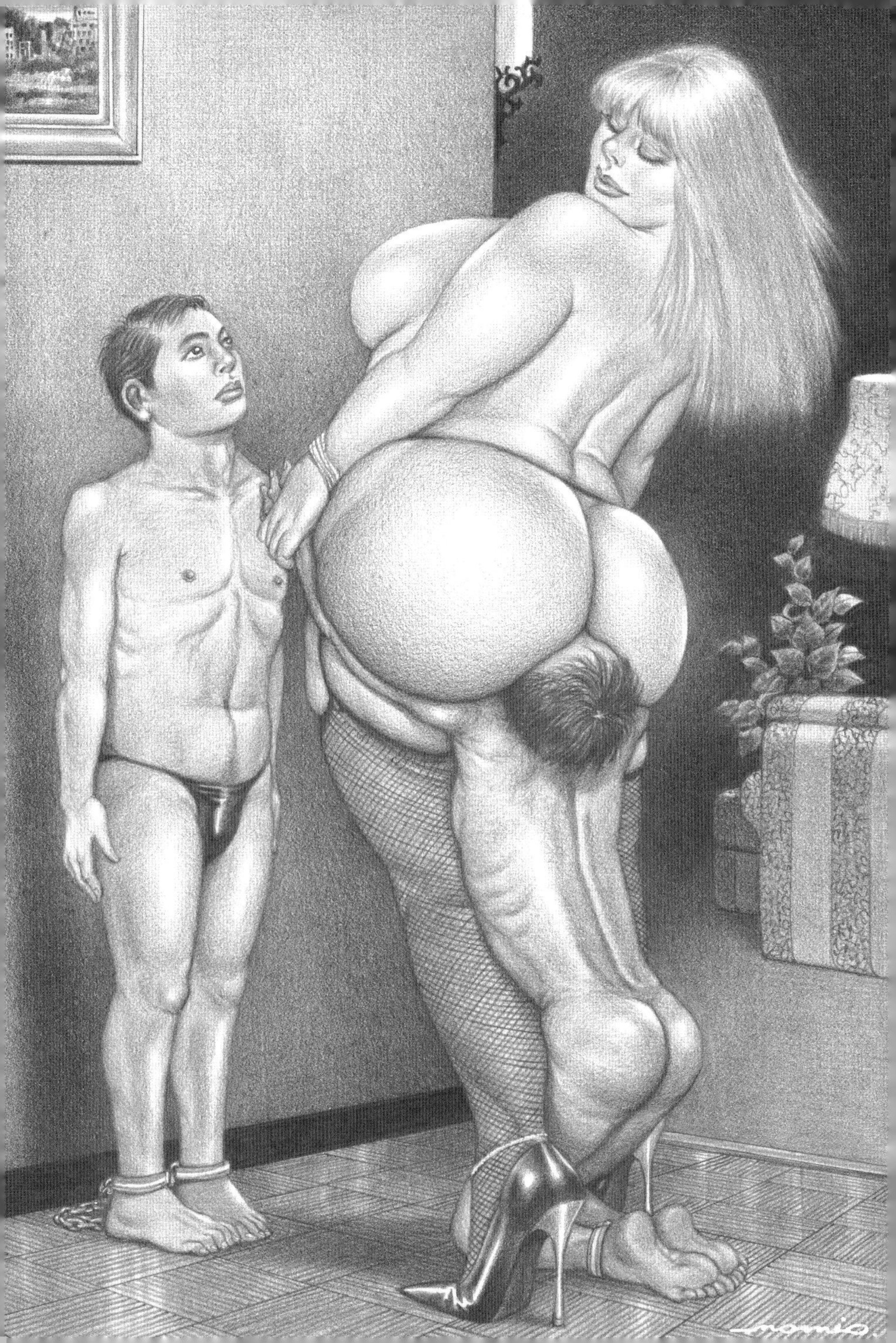

元アメリカ代表の巨大ヒップの肉壁に、十分に調教を受けた男たちもなす術なく失神した。
キャメロンはバスタブに浸かりながら、失神するまで自分のお尻に挟まれていた小さな日本の男を思い出しワクワクした。
男たちは、バスタオルを持って浴室の前に待機し、キャメロンが出てくると、巨大な全身を拭き、正座して命令を待った。
「サア、私ヲ気持チヨクサセテチョウダイ」
跪く男たちの前で両足を大きく広げると、男たちは恐る恐る巨大クレバスに顔をつけ、剛毛を舌で掻き分け、夢中で舐め続けた。
「オオ、イイワ、最高ヨ！　モット、モット、オ舐メ。ソノママ、下ヘ降リテ、オ尻ノ穴ヲオ舐メ。ソコヨ、トッテモ感ジル！！」

Although well-trained, the men had no recourse when faced with the former All-Star player's meaty hips. As Cameron lay in the bathtub, she excitedly recalled the small Japanese men whom she'd made faint with the tight grasp of her *oshiri*.
Meanwhile, the men waited outside the bathroom with bath towels in hand. When she emerged from the bath, they dried off her gigantic body, then they knelt on the floor awaiting Cameron's orders.
"Hey! You boys are gonna make me feel rreaalll nice an' good, ya hear me now?"
She opened her legs wide in front of the submissively genuflecting men. Fearfully, they pressed their faces into her gigantic crevice. Then they pushed their tongues through the thick growth and lost themselves in their licking.
"Go, guys, go! This is fuckin' good. Gimme more! Gimme more! Now, git your tongues down there lower. Lick my asshole!! Raagght there! You got me feelin' damn gooood."

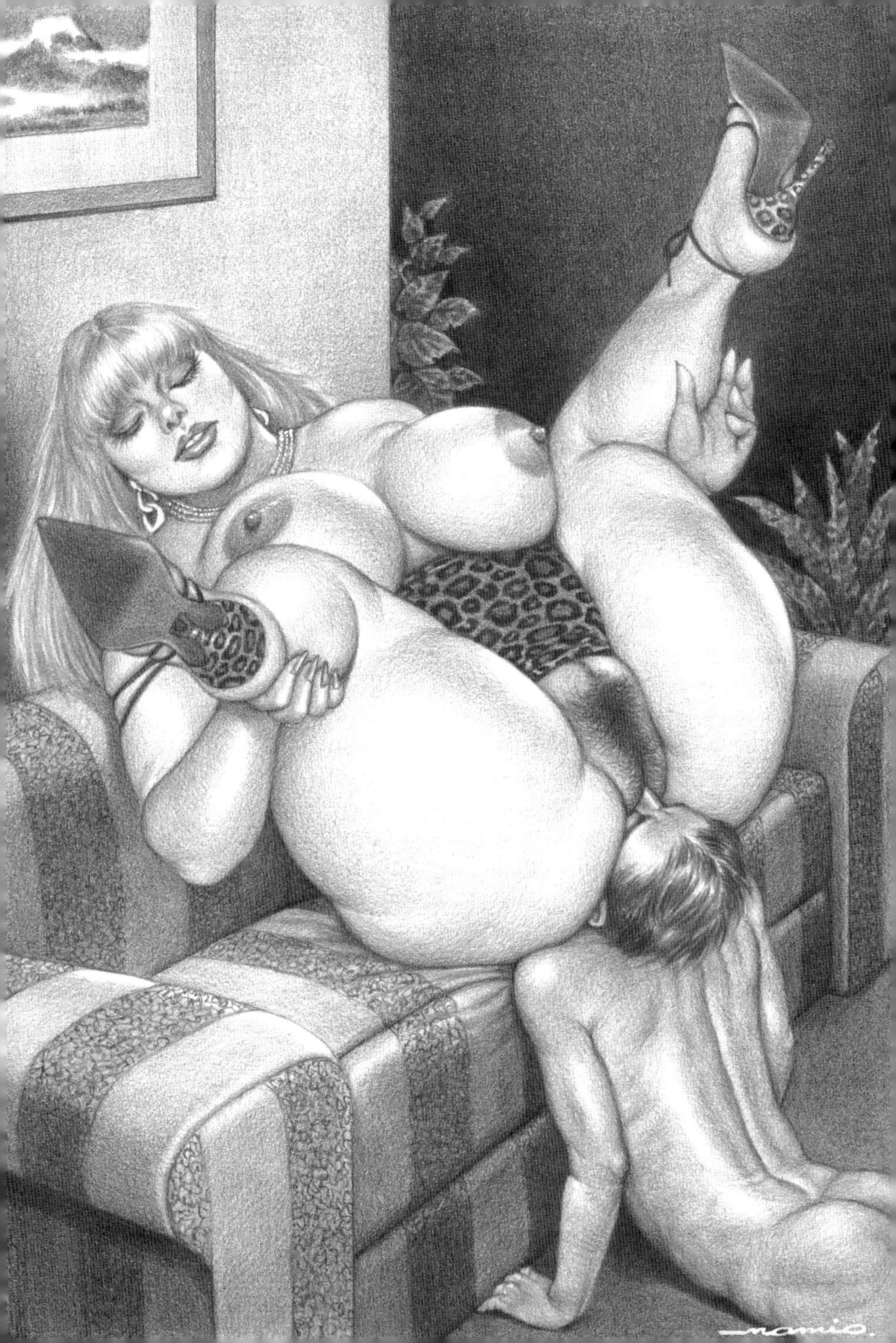

絶対服従を誓い、懸命に奉仕する日本の男の愛しさに、残虐性をエスカレートさせたキャメロンは、加奈から預かったムチを取り出した。レザーの服に着替え、男たちに首輪をつけると、2人に名前を尋ねた。そうして、片足を台に乗せ、秘部を露にすると、英男の首輪のひもを引き寄せ、舐めるように命じた。英男は懸命に舌を動かすも、もっと舌を深く入れるように、キャメロンはさらに強くひもを引く。と同時に、友三の背中を目がけてムチを振り下ろした。ピシッピシッ!!　あまりの痛みに友三がのけぞり、呻き声をあげる。
「ホホホ、気持チイイワ。両方トモ、イイワ。ソレ、モウ一発!」
鞭を振り下ろしながら、キャメロンは密着する英男の口に思い切り排泄した。

Her brutality exacerbated by the pitiful sight of these Japanese men who swore to her their complete submission, Cameron reached for the whip Kana had lent her. She changed into her leather, put collars around the men's necks, and asked for their names. Positioning one leg on a stand and exposing her pud, the American pulled on the leash attached to Hideo's collar and ordered him to lick. Even though he moved his tongue most determinedly, Cameron pushed him to tongue her deeper, yanking the leash even harder. When Yuzo's back caught her eye, she brought the whip down over and over. Literally bowled on his back by the whipping Yuzo let out a groan.
"Yeah, guys, this sure is fun. You slaves are both real fine. Now, here's some more of that whip for ya." As she brought the lash down again, she discharged herself completely into Hideo's pressing mouth.

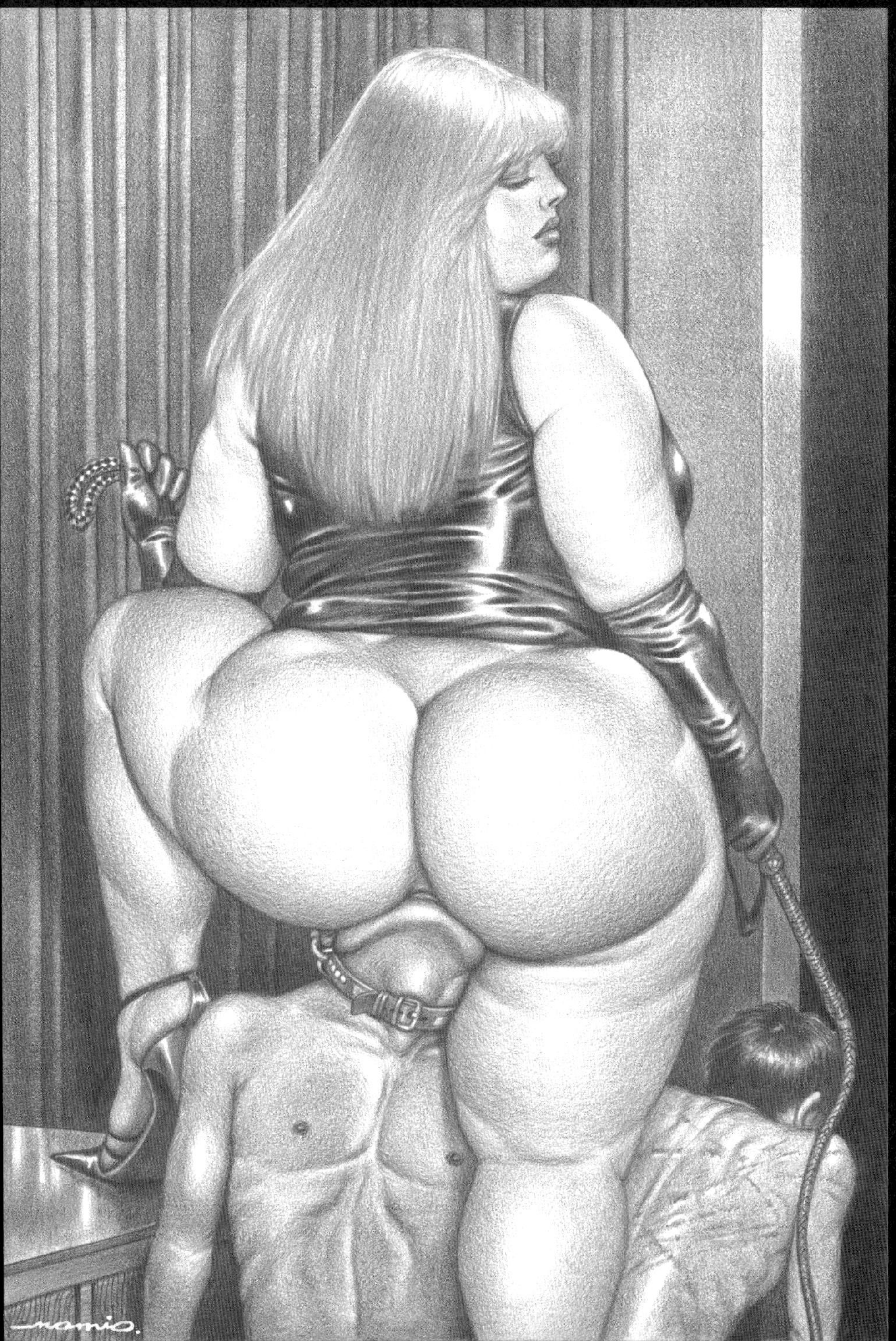
namio.

小柄な男の背にムチを振り下ろしては、聖水を注ぎ、黄金を食べさせる。忠実な2人のしもべは、すべてに応えキャメロンを満足させ、キャメロンは寝食を忘れ、男たちを責め続けた。
やがて、キャメロンは休憩をとるため、英男を台にして、その上に友三の頭を乗せた人間椅子になることを命じた。
座面となった友三に巨大なヒップが迫る。割れ目の奥には恥毛に囲まれたアヌスが茶褐色に輝き蠢いている。友三の顔はゆっくりと巨尻に包まれ、キャメロンの体重を支える。
「友三ノ顔ガ、スッポリオ尻ニ埋マッタワ。イイワネ」
重圧にもがき苦しむ友三のヴァイヴレーションに酔うキャメロンは、失神したことにも気づかず、コーヒーを味わった。

Unleashing the whip upon the backs of the little men, filling them with her holy water, having them eat her gold—Cameron's every wish was satisfied so well by these two faithful slaves that she forgot about eating or sleeping and continued to abuse them on and on, further and further.
So that she might take a break, however, Cameron ordered the two men to form a human chair for her, Hideo becoming a small table and Yuzo lying face-up on the surface Hideo made.
The tremendous hips approached Yuzo, who had become the seat to this human chair. Deep in the crack, surrounded by her pubic hair, Cameron's anus twinkled a light brown. Yuzo's face was slowly buried in her tremendous buttocks as he supported her full weight.
"Youzoh! Yer frickin' face is frickin' right up my ass. And thaat is dammnn gooood."
Enraptured by the vibrations emanating from Yuzo's body, writhing as it was under her heavy load, Cameron sipped her coffee not noticing that Yuzo had, in fact, fainted.

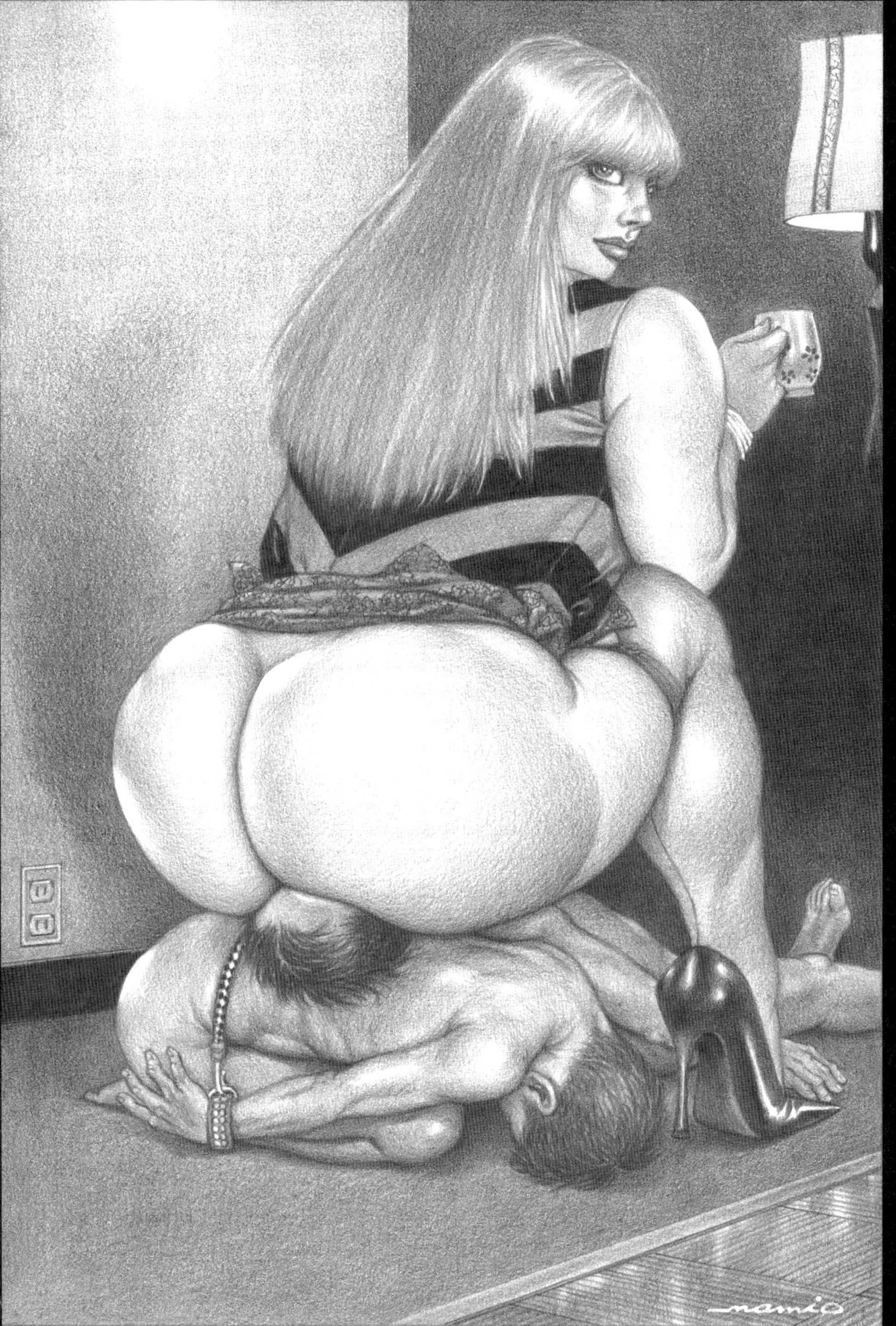
namio

帰国したキャメロンは日本での素晴らしい体験を、元バレーボールブラジル代表で、現在は大農場を経営するジュリアに話した。すると、さっそくジュリアも日本にやって来た。
宿泊先の高級ホテルのスイートルームに派遣された2人の男は、世界一巨大な美女と賞賛される、身長2m10cm、バスト150cm、ヒップ180cm、ブロンズ色に輝く肌に彫りの深い顔立ちのジュリアを見上げて驚いた。
へたり込む男の首輪のひもを握ると、すばやく跨ぎ、ひもを引き、自身の繁みに男の顔を押し当てた。
「サア、挨拶代ワリニ、キスシナサイ」
男は巨大なプッシーに夢中で舌を伸ばす。
「加奈カラ君タチノコトハ聞イテイルワ。安心ナサイ、殺シハシナイカラ、フフフ。デモ私ノ命令ニ背イタラ殺スカモヨ、ホホホ」

Once she was back in the States, Cameron told others about her wonderful experience in Japan, including Julia, a fellow former volleyball star who had played for the All-Brazil team. Although Julia was busy running a large farm, she too found time to make the voyage. The two men dispatched to Julia's luxury suite in a top-class hotel were stunned to behold the largest beauty in the world. In addition to her stunning figures—she was 210 cm tall, with a bust of 150 cm and hips of 180 cm, Julia had beautifully chiseled features and a glistening, bronze skin.
She grasped the leashes on the two cowering men, and quickly straddled them, pulling their faces towards her own pubic thicket. "Sooo, my deeears, no greeeeting neeeeded. Just kiiiesss meeee heeere." Julia spoke in a lovely, Luso-Brazilian melody.
As if sharing a trance, the men stuck out their tongues towards the massive pussy. "My deeeaar Kaanaah, sheee has told meee olll abooot youuh. Sooo, don't beee wahhhried. I wiiielll not kiiielll youuh. Teee, heee, heee. Baatt, eeeif youuh dooo not beehaaave, maybeee I doooh. Teee, heee, heee."

[210 cm = 6'10" / 150 cm = 59" / 180 cm =71"]

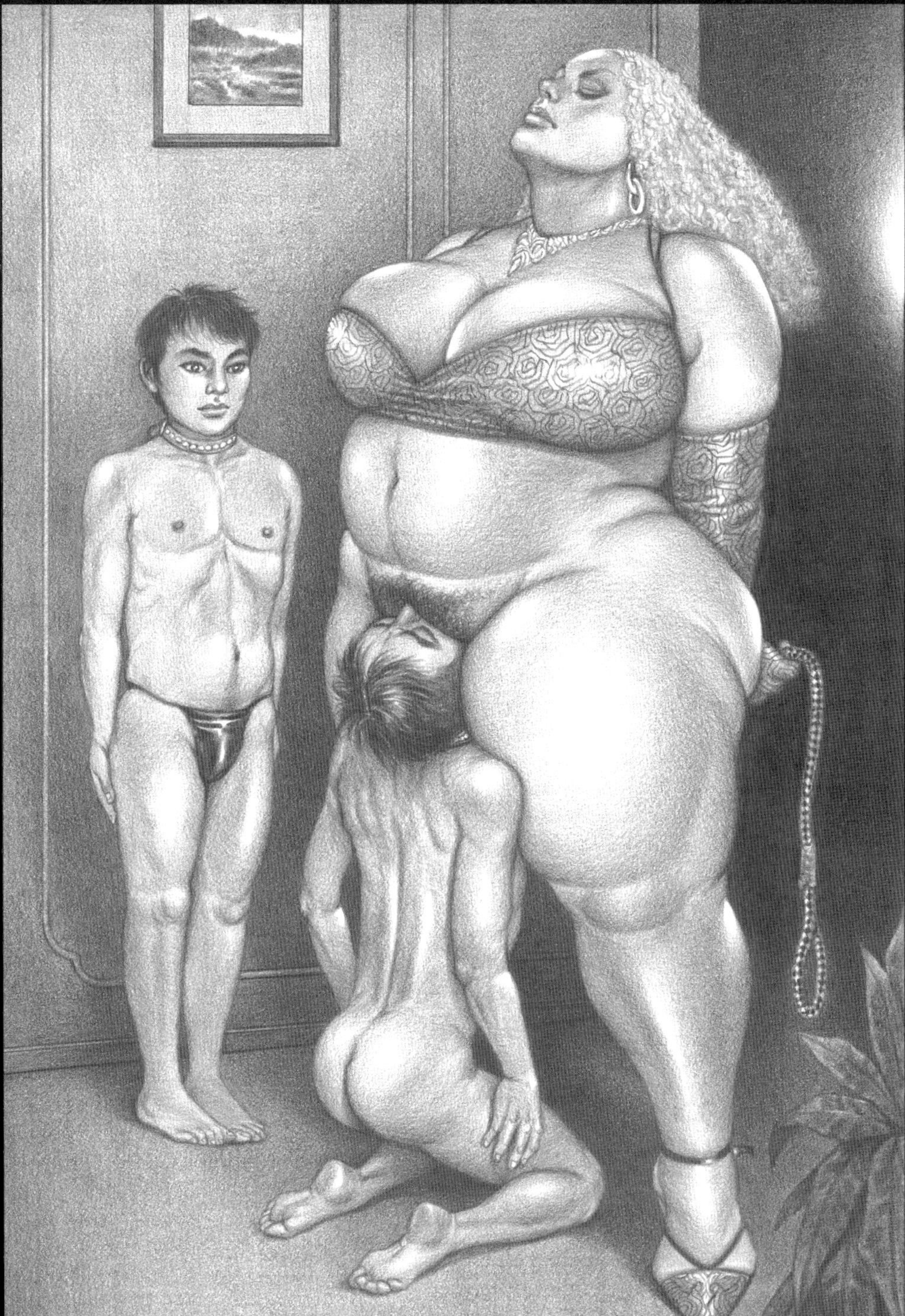

慎太郎と道夫が挨拶を済ますと、ジュリアはヒップを剥き出してソファに横座りした。
「慎太郎、オ尻ヲ、早ク、オ舐メナサイ」
慎太郎は必死で舌を伸ばすが、肉の谷は深くアヌスに届かない。ジュリアは慎太郎の腕を尻に敷き押さえ込むと、お尻を開き、慎太郎の顔を押し込んだ。
そのとき、加奈が訪ねてきた。
「ハーイ、加奈。美シクナッタワネ。アナタの事業ハ海外デモ噂ニナッテイルワヨ」
「ありがとう。実はすごい計画があるの。熱烈なファンからゴルフ場をプレゼントされたのよ。それで、思い切ってゴルフ場を全部、楽園に改造しようと思うの」
「スゴイワ。青空ノ下デ、コンナコトガデキルダナンテ夢ノヨウダワ。楽シミネ」
慎太郎が失神しているのも忘れて、2人の会話ははずんだ。

When Shintaro and Michio had finished their greeting, Julia bared her hips and spread out on the sofa. "Sheentarohh! Harrry up to lieecckk meee *oshiri*." Shintaro desperately proffered his tongue, but the meaty valley was so deep, he could not reach her anus. Julia pulled Shintaro's arm into her *oshiri*. Thus opening it, she forced Shintaro's face inside.
It was just then that Kana made her appearance.
"My deeeaar Kaanaah! Youuh ahre eeeeven moooore beeyuuteeeful. And, weee heeear olll abooot your werrk."
"Why, thank you! Actually, I've been hammering out a great new plan. One of my big fans has given me a golf course. And I am thinking of totally reconstructing the place as a new Garden of Paradise for us."
"Kaanaah! To beee able to dooo zhis in zee oooopen airrr. Whaaatt a dreeeam! I cannot waaeeettt."
Forgetting that Shintaro had passed out, the two pursued their lively conversation.

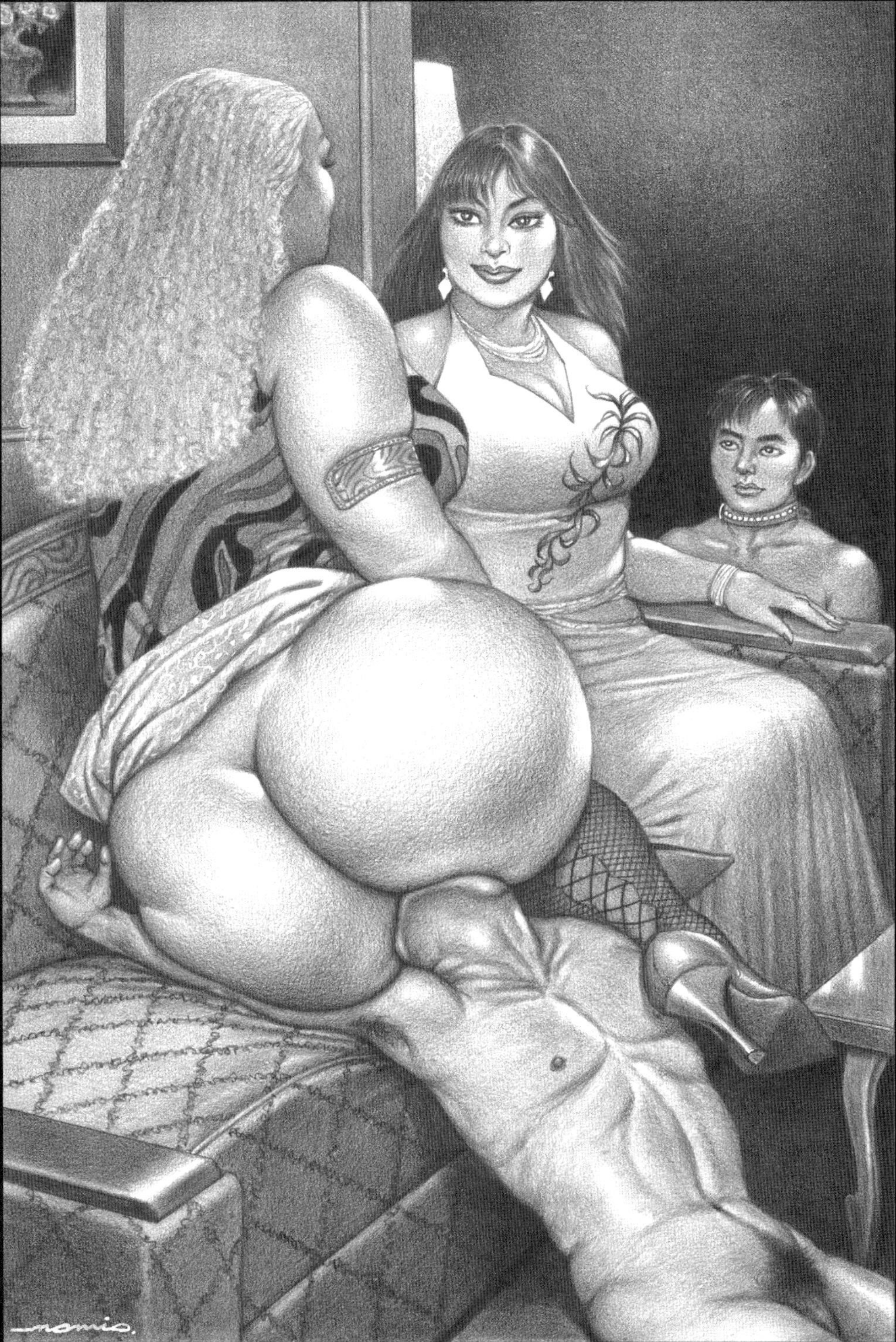

加奈とジュリアの話は尽きない。これまで出会った男たち —— 巨尻の下で一生を送りたいと願う男、舌が動かなくなるまで奉仕する男、100発のムチ打ちに失神した男、人間便器になりたい男、等々、加奈の話と忠実な日本の男たちの奉仕に、ジュリアは自身のS的性格にはじめて気づかされた。

ジュリアはスツールに座り慎太郎を尻に敷きながらワインを味わい、会話の余韻と慎太郎がもがく感触に浸っていた。巨大ヒップに挟まれた小さな慎太郎は、ほどなく動かなくなった。

There was no end to what Kana and Julia could talk about. The men they'd met so far: men who wanted to live their lives under their tremendous buttocks, men who would service until their tongues could move no more, men who fainted but only after a hundred lashes of the whip, men who would be human toilets, such men… listening to Kana's words and experiencing the service of Japan's faithful men, Julia began to recognize her own sadistic nature.

Julia was sitting on a stool drinking wine; she had positioned Shintaro right beneath her *oshiri*. What a pleasure to enjoy the mood of the conversation and feel at the same Shintaro's writhing beneath her. Before long, the puny Shintaro, pinned down by her massive hips, stopped moving.

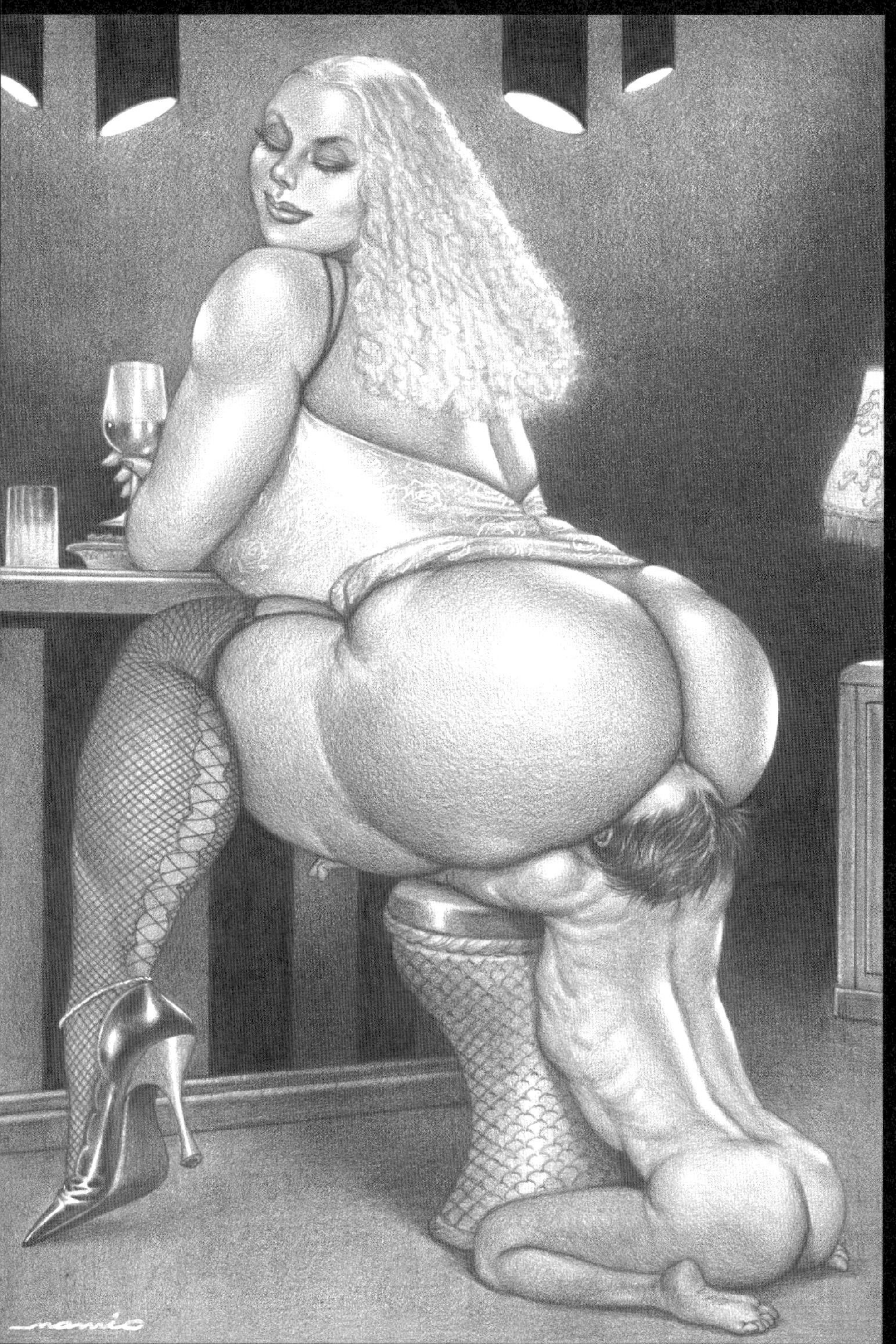
namio

ジュリアの巨尻の下で何度も失神を繰り返した慎太郎と道夫は、休む間もなくバスルームに呼ばれ、仁王立ちで2人を見下ろすジュリアの神々しい体を、喜々として洗った。その様を見てジュリアは巨体をゆすって高笑いする。
2人掛りで体を洗い終えると、ジュリアは裸でベッドに横たわり、2人を呼んだ。
「道夫ハ前、慎太郎ハ後ロヲ奉仕シナサイ」
ジュリアは2人の男根を縄で縛り、逃げられないように繋げた。
「サァ、2人トモ、舌ヲ奥マデ入レテゴラン。前モ後ロモ感ジル。オ前タチハ最高ヨ。サア、口ヲ開ケナサイ。同時ニスルワヨ。シッカリオ飲ミ、シッカリオ食ベ!!」

Shintaro and Michio had lost consciousness countless times now beneath Julia's massive buttocks. But there would be no rest for the weary; they were summoned to the bathroom. Julia stood with her two legs spread and looked down, not without some scorn, while they merrily scrubbed her godlike body. Amused at the scene, Julia swayed from side to side and laughed aloud.
When the pair's duty of cleaning her body was complete, Julia lay herself down naked upon the bed.
"Meecheeoh, in zee frontt, and Sheentarohh in zee bacckk. Nowww, seeurviice meee.
She tied their two cocks with rope, connecting them so they couldn't get away.
"Noww, youu both. Putt zee taaangue in deeep. I feeel goood in zee frontt and in zee bacckk. You aaahr greaayt. Noww, ooopen zee mouth. I doo both togezzer. Youuh eeatt it oolll and youuh dreeenkk it ooolll.

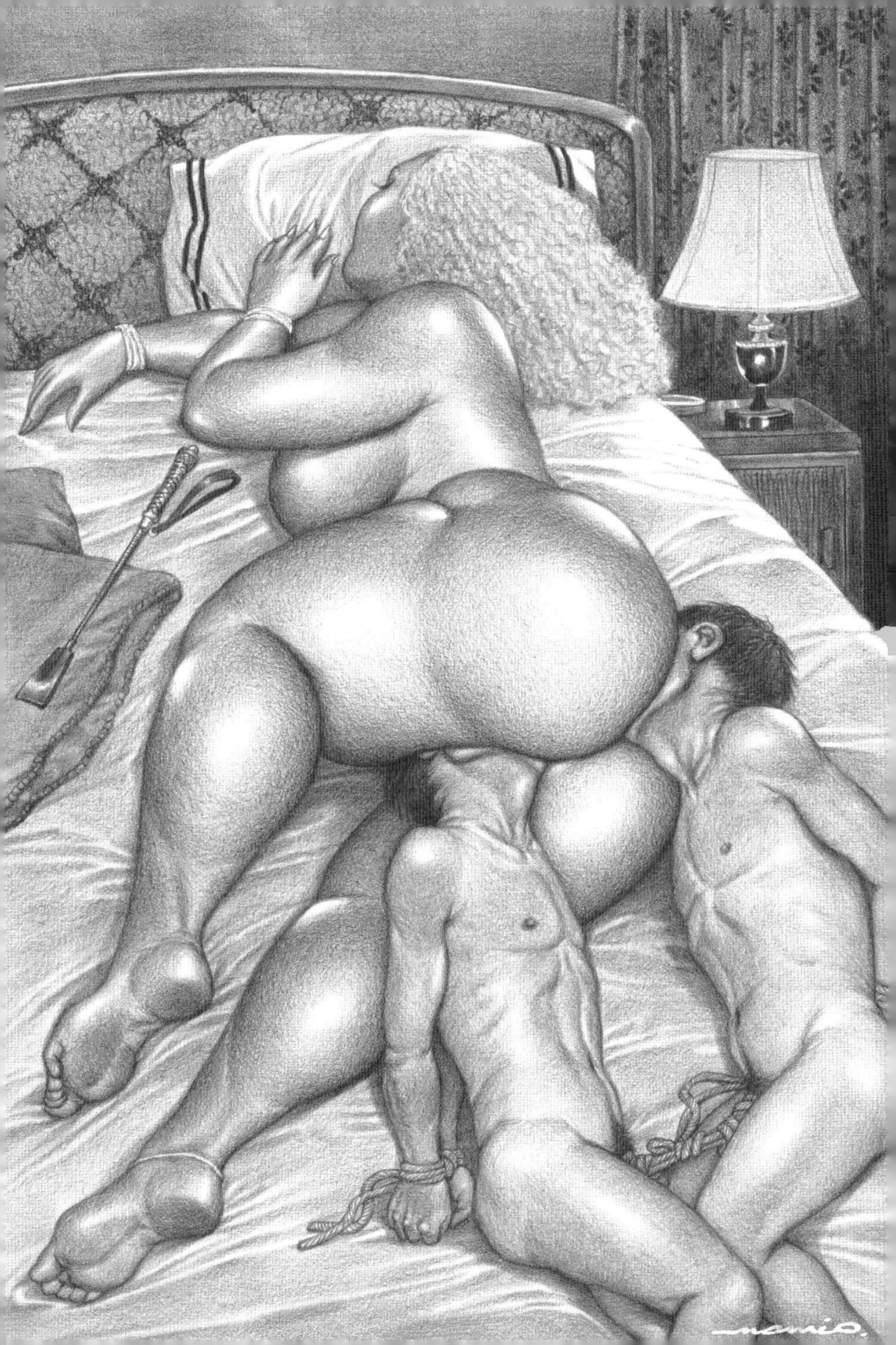

雄大な自然を活かしたNOBUカントリークラブのオーナー石田信男は大原加奈を女神と崇め、加奈のお尻の下で圧死することに憧れ、ゴルフ場をはじめとする全財産を加奈に献上し、専属奴隷になることを許された。
「広くて気持ちいいわね、信男」
「加奈様にお気に入りいただき光栄でございます」
「太陽の下で、美しい女神たちが思う存分、男たちと戯れるかと思うとワクワクするわ」
「太陽の楽園」は、専属女性スタッフ30人、奴隷50人を擁する女性のための屋外アミューズメント施設で、オープンを1週間後に控えていた。ここは全ての女性に開かれ、利用者たちは、その美しさを誇示するため下半身を完全露出が原則で、男性は適正を認められた者のみが入場を許され、女性を崇拝し絶対服従することが義務づけられた。

The owner of the Nobu Country Club with its impressive views of its natural surroundings was Ishida Nobuo. Nobu worshipped Ohara Kana as if she were a goddess. Nobu longed to be crushed to death under Kana's *oshiri*, and he gave over to Kana his entire estate, beginning with the golf course. In turn, he was allowed to become Kana's dedicated, personal slave.
"It's so wide, and it feels so good out here, Nobu."
"I'm just happy that it might please Mistress Kana."
"It's exciting to think that beautiful Goddesses might toy with their men in the open sunlight—and to their hearts content."
A week later, Sun Paradise would be opening as an outdoor amusement facility with a dedicated staff of thirty women and fifty slaves. Open to all women, its guests would be required to show off their beauty, and for that reason expected to expose their lower halves. Only men considered appropriate to the venue would be admitted. Such men were required to worship and to be completely obedient to women.

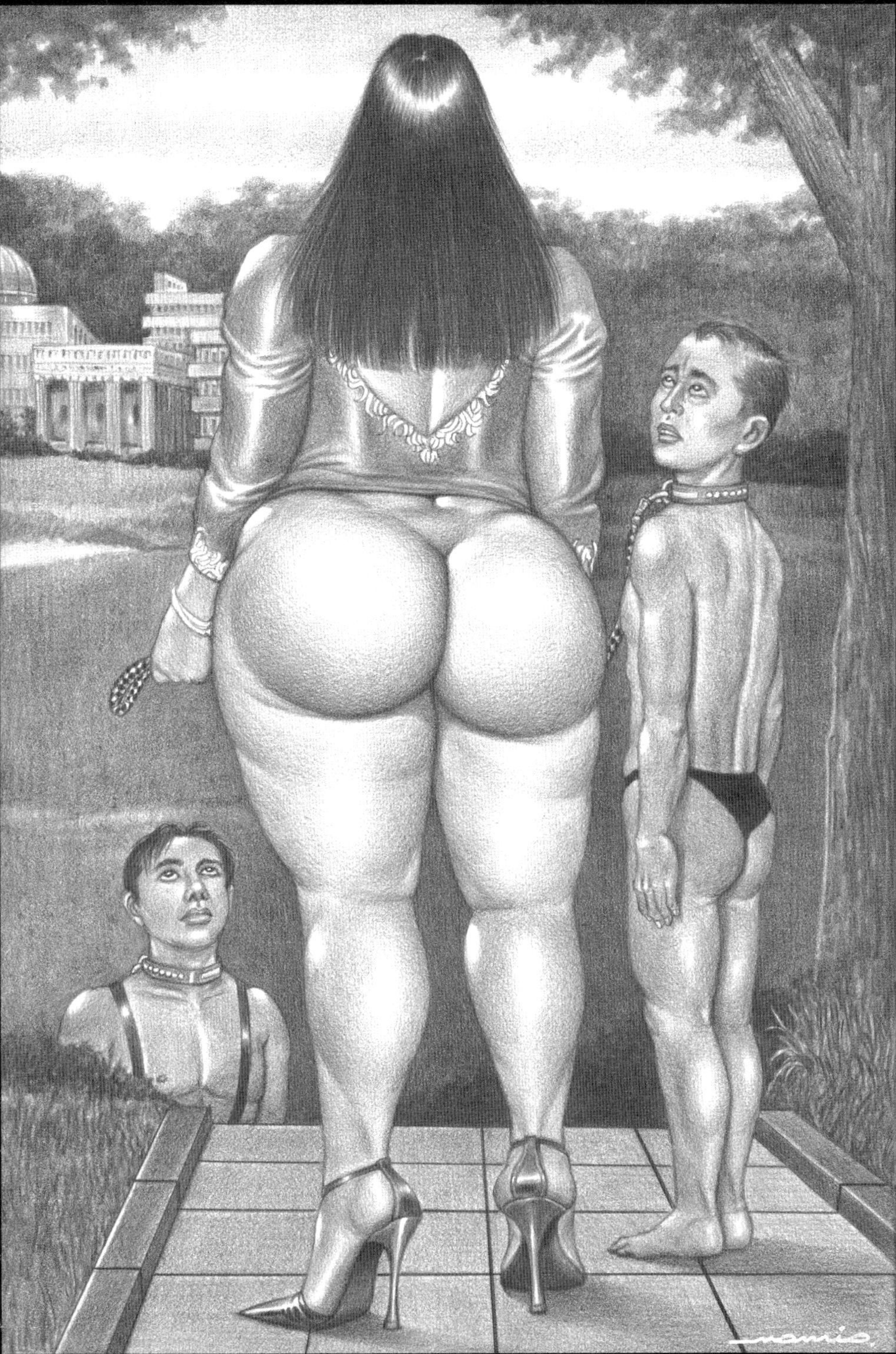

楽園では、女性が移動するときのために、首に特製サドルを取り付けた男たちが配置されている。加奈は、乗馬ムチを手に、跪いて待ち受ける男のサドルに跨がり試乗する。
男は顔をまっ赤にして120kgの加奈を乗せて立ち上がったが、巨大なお尻に顔を挟まれて踏み出すことができない。ピシッ！　ピシッ!!　男の背中にムチが飛ぶ。
「歩いてごらん、ほら。私より大きな御婦人が乗ったらどうするの。お前の役目は何なの?」
男は踏ん張って前に進むが10mほどで潰れてしまった。加奈は、すぐに2人目に乗り換えたが、またしても10mも歩けない。
「もう、この広いグリーンを歩けっていうの。いいわ、お前たち、並んで四つん這いにおなり!!」
2頭立ての男たちの背中に跨がると、加奈はムチを振り下ろし、お尻の下で男たちがもがきながら懸命に前進した。

In this Paradise, men were positioned here and there with specially built saddles around their necks so that women could use them to move about. With a crop in her hands, Kana straddled the saddle of one kneeling, waiting man in order to give it a try.
His face bright red, the man was able to stand and carry Kana's 120 kilos, but with his face enveloped entirely in her buttocks, he couldn't manage even a step forward. Swissh. Swissh. The crop rained down upon his back.
"Get going and try walking. What would you do if it weren't me but a Lady customer? You know your purpose here!"
The man exerted himself again and managed to push forward, but having only gone ten meters, he collapsed. Kana quickly mounted another, but he too could only go about ten meters.
"Are you telling me I should walk this long green? I've had enough of you. Stand in position next to each other, then get on all fours."
Kana mounted this two-men carriage, and brought the crop down hard; struggling under the weight of her *oshiri*, the men desperately edged forward.

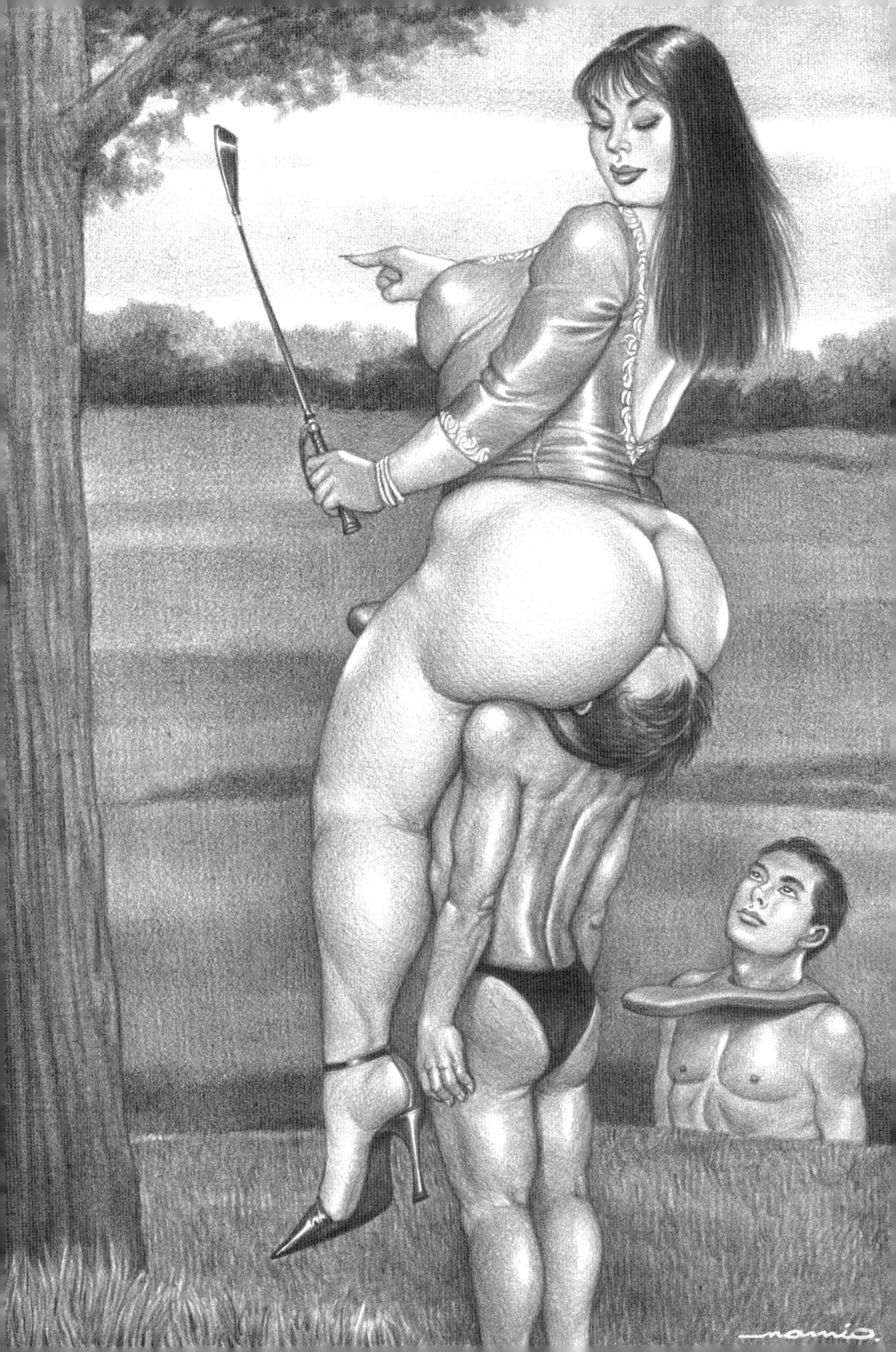

グリーン手前の芝生には人間椅子が設置されていた。低い丸太椅子の前に掘られた穴には男が入っていて、女性に座っていただくために頭を丸太の上に乗せ待っているのである。加奈が近づいて来ると、男は緊張と歓喜に目を見開き受け入れ態勢を作る。加奈が座ると、重圧から男がうめき声をあげた。加奈はコーヒーを飲みながら、男の顔の感触をお尻で確かめる。
「思った以上に座り心地がいいわ。さすが人間椅子専門男だけあるわね。高さも丁度だわ」
加奈は男の頭を押さえながら、巨尻を揺する。
「苦しくても、頭を動かして御婦人を落とさないように気をつけることね」
男は苦しさにもがき出す。
「その苦しむ姿が楽しいのよ。あらあら殺しそうだわ。まだまだ訓練が必要ね」
加奈は腰をあげると、案内係の女性に、人間便器と間違われないように、人間椅子の表示を出すように指示して、移動した。

On the grass right before the green, some human-chairs had been set up. One man had been lowered into a small trench where he waited, resting his head on a log chair so that a passing woman might sit upon it. Seeing Kana approach, his eyes opened with nervousness and delight, and he positioned himself better to receive her. When she sat, he groaned with the weight. And, while she drank her coffee, she used her *oshiri* to inspect the feel of his face.
"This is more comfortable for sitting than I had imagined. Leave it to a specially trained human chair to make sitting feel so good. And the height is just right." Kana held the man's head down and began to rock her ample buttocks. "Even if it's hard on you, you've got to move your head to make sure you don't drop the Lady." The man began writhing in pain.
"It's such fun to see you suffering. Uh oh! I've almost killed you. You need more training, it seems." Kana lifted her waist, and instructed a woman staffmember from guest services to erect a sign to make sure the human chair would not be mistaken for a human toilet. Kana then moved on.

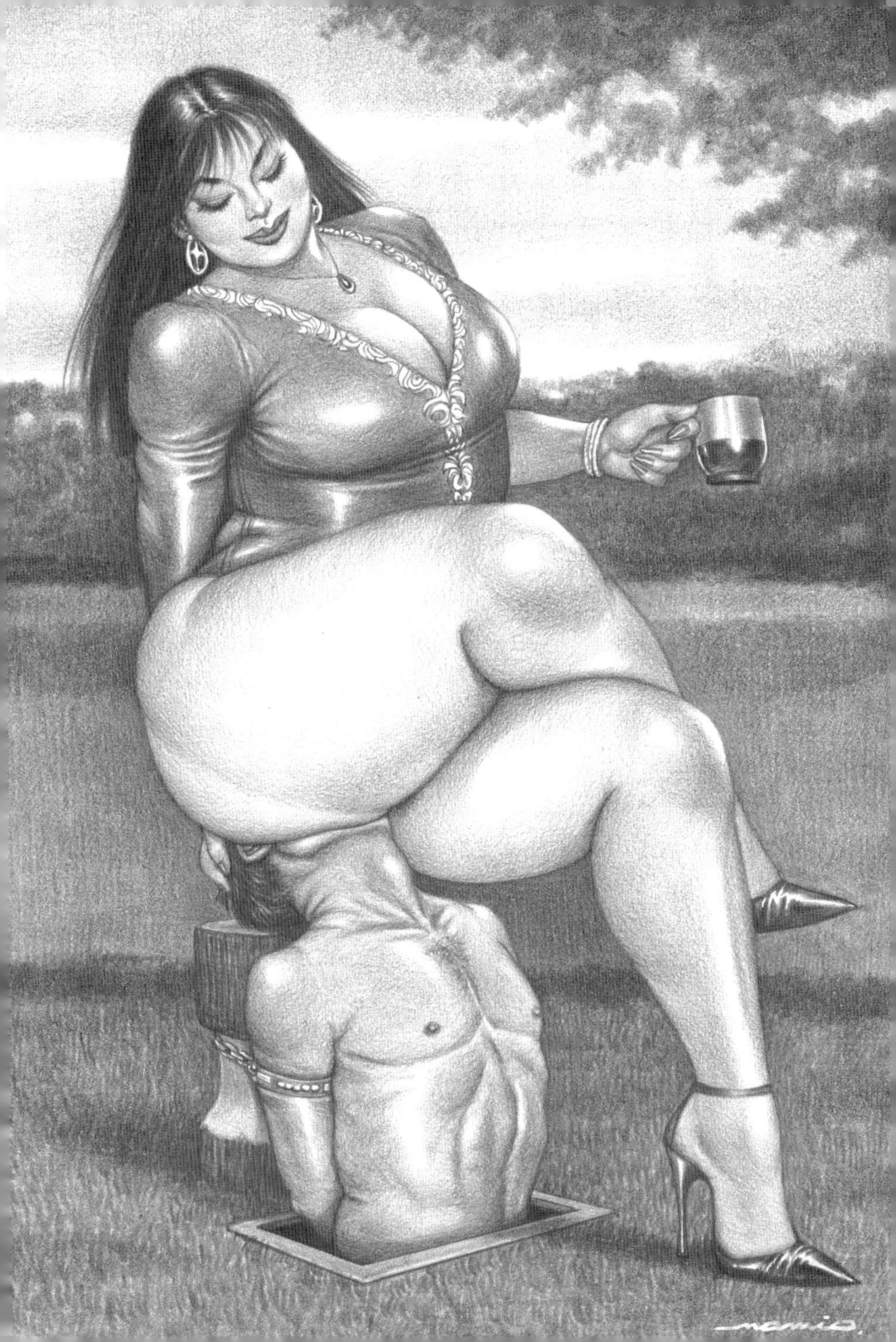

次に加奈は人間便器へと向かった。パラソルの下、2本の丸太の間に穴が掘られ、男が顔を出しているシンプルな設計だ。丸太に取り付けられた便座に腰下ろし、待ち受ける金髪の白人男の顔に巨尻を突き出す。
「はじめにお尻の穴をお舐め。そうして出やすくするのよ。いいわ、舌の動かし方が上手ね」
男は巨尻におののきながら舌を必死で動かす。
「そう、次にぴったり口をつけて吸ってごらん。ああ、出るわ。しっかり、お食べ」
加奈のお尻と男の口が密着し隠れてはいるが、激しい男の喉の動きから状況がわかる。
「とても気持いいわ。上級の人間便器ね。合格よ。日本人男性も見習ったらいいわ」
加奈はゆっくり立ち上がると、横で待機する男の顔の前に巨尻を出して命じた。
「後始末をなさい!!」

Kana headed next towards the human-toilets. These had a simple design, protected by a parasol: from a hole that had been dug between two short, vertical logs, a man's face appeared. When Kana sat upon the toilet seat, secured between the two logs, her massive buttocks protruded out towards a waiting blond-haired Caucasian man. "First, lick the hole to my *oshiri*. Make things easier to pass. You've got very good technique in your tongue motion."
Trembling at the tremendous buttocks, the man passionately moved his tongue.
"Next place your mouth right there and begin to suck. Oh, it's coming. Eat it all up."
The tight connection between Kana's *oshiri* and the man's mouth may have concealed what was happening, but everything was obvious from the man's furious movement of his throat.
"That felt very good. You're a top-class human-toilet. You pass. Japanese men have something to learn from you."
Kana stood up slowly, and stuck her *oshiri* into the face of a man who had been waiting by the side. She ordered, "Now, you here, tidy me up."

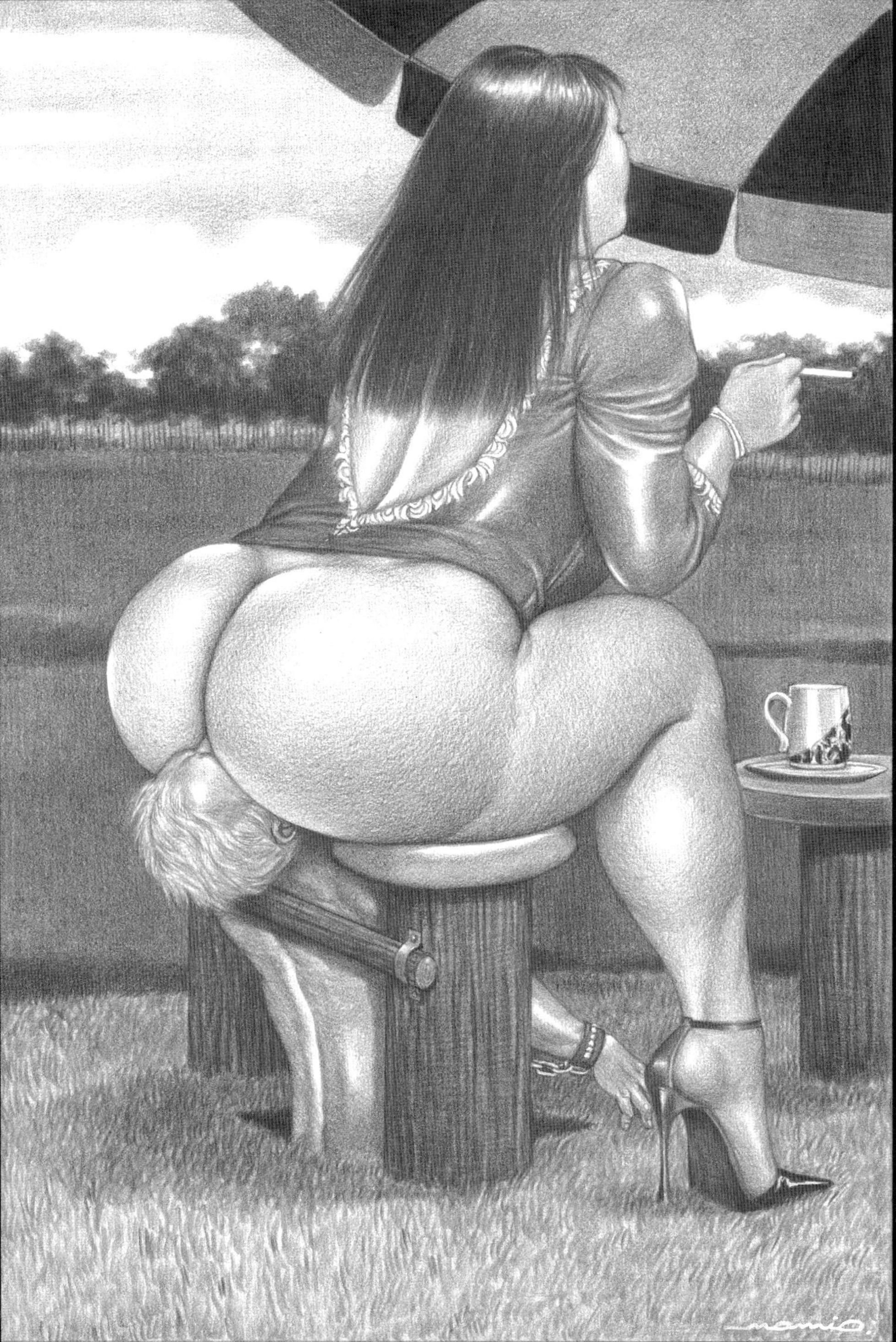

"太陽の楽園"がオープンした。銀座で宝石店を経営する川崎礼子がさっそくやって来た。サロンやレンタル男を愛用する、豊満な貴婦人である。会員登録をして、年会費を払えば楽園をいつでも利用できる。礼子は手続きを済ますと、男たちが待つ部屋に案内された。ここで、その日の専属奴隷になる男を選ぶことができるのである。
「川崎様、お気に入りの男の顔の前でお尻を突き出してください。服従を誓う儀式として、お尻にキスをいたします」
正座して待つ15人ほどの男をじっくり品定めし、礼子は一人の男の前で振り向くとお尻を突き出した。
「さあ、お尻の穴にキスなさい」
男は大きなお尻を拝みながら、ゆっくりと舌を伸ばした。

Sun Paradise was finally open. Kawasaki Reiko, who managed a jewelry shop in the Ginza, quickly paid a visit. A frequent patron of the Salon and of rental-men, Reiko was a voluptuous lady. At Sun Paradise, if a woman completed the membership registration and paid the yearly fee, she could visit as frequently she liked. Once Reiko had completed the paperwork she was shown to a room where the men were waiting for the visitors. It was there that she would be able to choose the slave who would be her personal slave for the day.
"Ms. Kawasaki, might I ask you to extend your *oshiri* towards the man that you'd like? As he swears his submission to you, he will ceremonially kiss your *oshiri*."
Reiko carefully sized up the fifteen men who were kneeling on the floor waiting. She tuned in front of one of them and pushed out her *oshiri*.
"Please kiss the *oshiri* hole."
Worshipping the large *oshiri* that was before him, the man slowly extended his tongue.

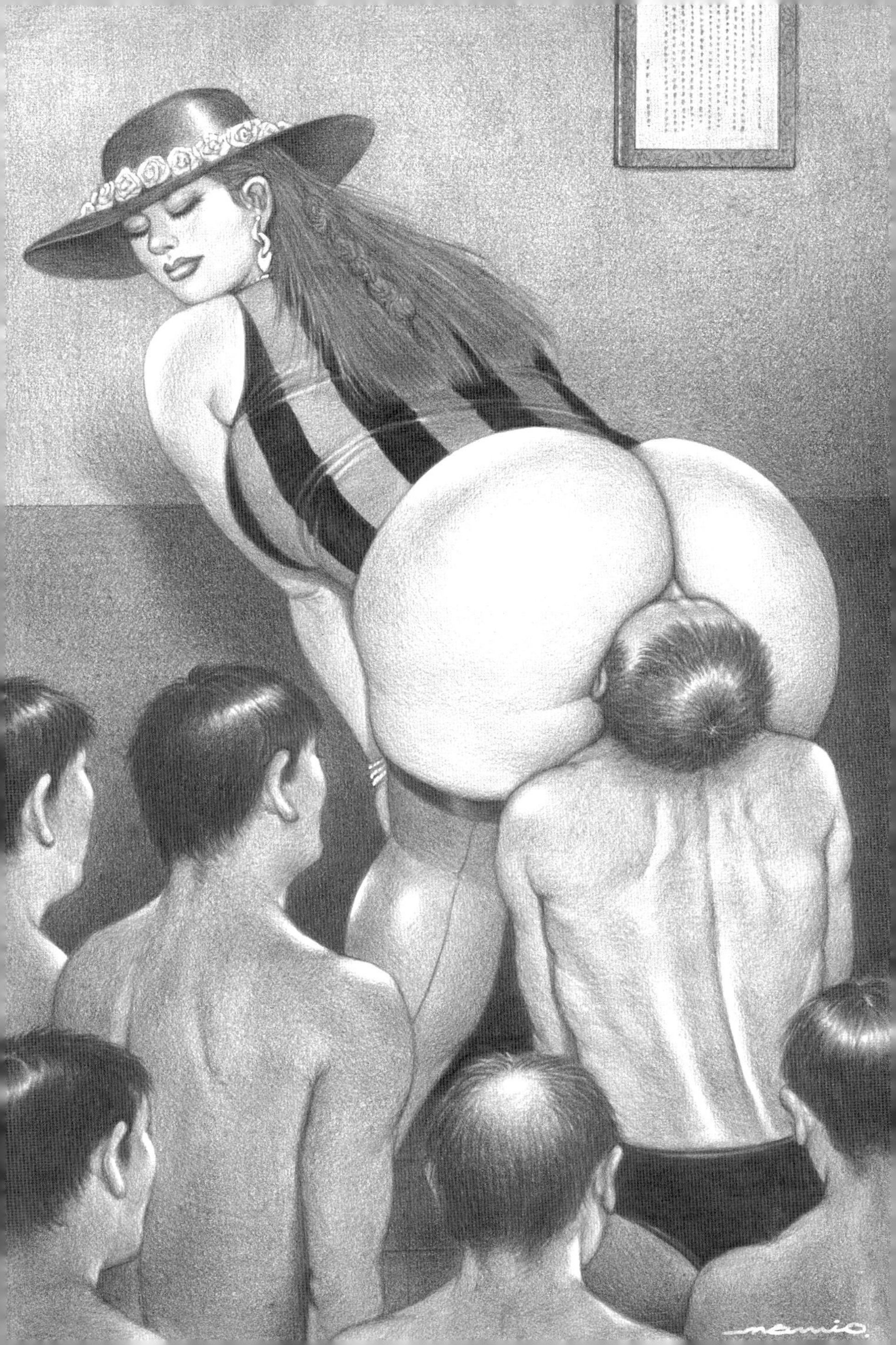
namio.

「日差しが気持ちいいし、君の顔も柔らかくてお尻がとっても気持ちいいわ」
礼子はグリーンの真ん中で男を敷きながらタバコをくゆらせてうっとりしていてた。
「名前は何ていうの?」
「久保田崇でございます」
「崇は今どんな気持ち?」
「美しいお尻に敷いていただき、とても幸せです」
「私の命令なら何でもきける?」
「はい、服従をお誓い申し上げます」
「それなら、私のお尻の下で死んでもらおうかしら」
「それだけはお許しください」
「ホホホ、殺さないわよ、でも、いつか私の大きなお尻の下で男を圧死させたいわ。それは楽しみにとっておくわ、さあ、舌で気持ちよくさせてちょうだい」

"The sunlight feels so warm, and my *oshiri* feels so good on your soft face." Reiko was enraptured by the moment, sitting with a man beneath her in the middle of the green and enjoying a cigarette.
"What's your name?"
"I'm Kubota Takashi, Mistress."
"Takashi, what are you feeling right now?"
"I am so happy that you have placed me beneath your beautiful *oshiri*."
"And you'll follow each of my commands?"
"Yes, I swear my obedience to you, Mistress."
"Shall I have you die beneath my *oshiri* then?"
"Please spare me that, Mistress!"
"Ha, ha, ha! Well, I shan't kill you. But some day, I do want to squash some man to death under my big *oshiri*. I'll save that for later. For now, you'd better get your tongue busy making me feel good."

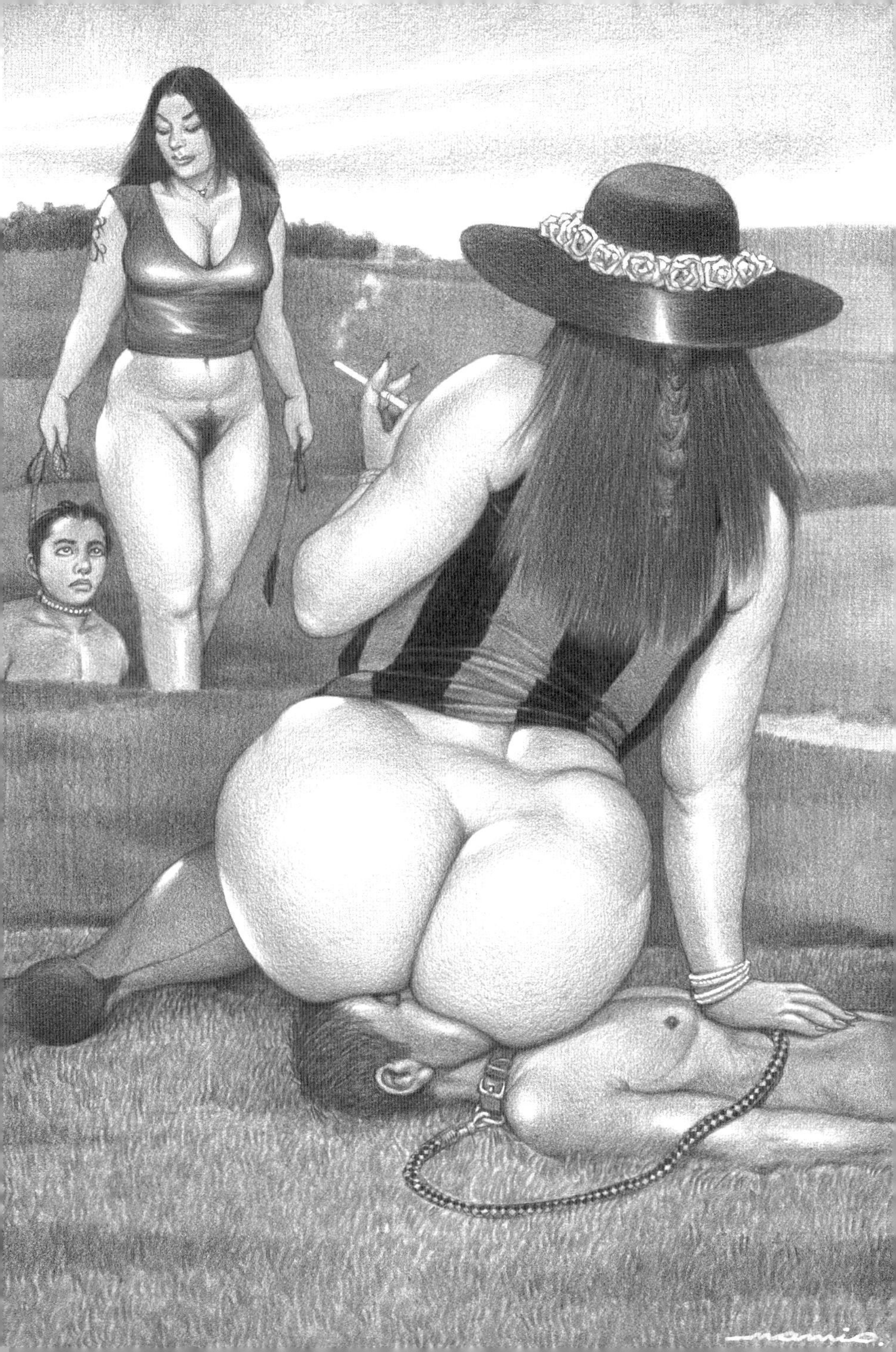

礼子は降り注ぐ日差しの下、崇の舌奉仕を楽しんだ。途中、口を開けさせ聖水を注いでやると、一滴もこぼさずに飲み干した。続いて黄金も与えようとすると、崇は答えた。
「申し訳ございませんが、私はまだB級で便器の調教中です」
そこで礼子は、専用便器を使うことにした。2本の丸太に両手を固定された男が、間の穴からヒップを見上げる座式の便器である。礼子が腰を落とすと、小さな男の顔がお尻に顔を埋めて礼子を支え、礼子の体の中に舌を伸ばし、ゆっくりと刺激する。
「もっと奥まで。あ、出そうよ、いくわよ」
男のノドがゆっくりと動き出した。

Basking in the sunlight, Reiko was thoroughly enjoying Takashi's tongue service. At one point, she had him open his mouth wide to grant him her holy water, and he downed it all without spilling a single drop. But, when she went to give him gold, Takashi spoke.
"I'm most terribly sorry, but I'm only a Class B man, so I'm still in training as a toilet."
Reiko decided then to use one of the dedicated toilets. A man was attached by his hands to two separate logs. From his positioning in a hole between the logs, he could look up and see the hips of the woman using this squat-style toilet. Reiko lowered herself, and the little man's face became buried in her *oshiri* as he actively supported her. He extended his tongue to reach inside Reiko's body and slowly stimulated her.
"Go deeper! Oh, it's coming. I've got to go!"
The man's throat began to slowly move.

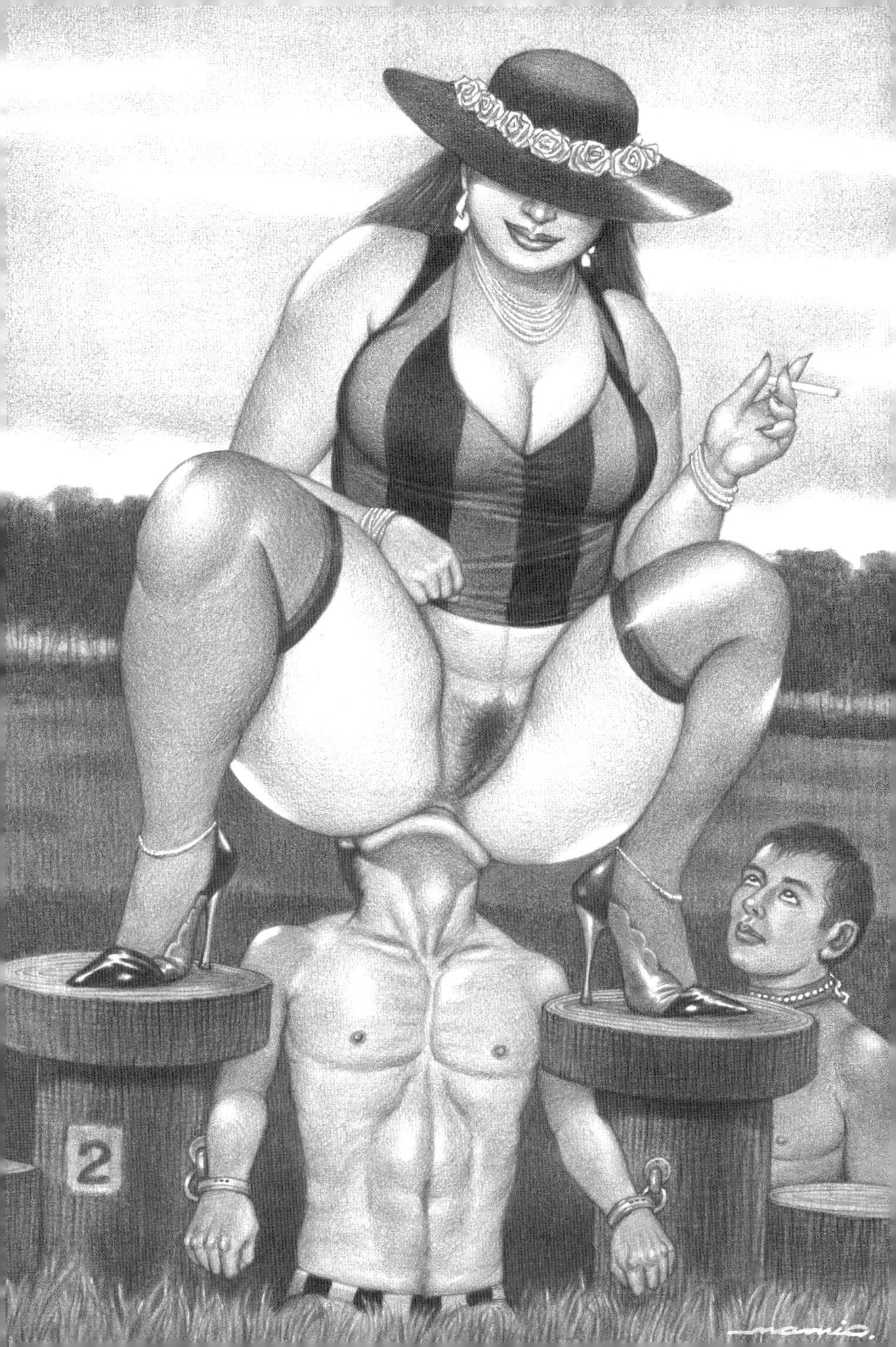
2

美しく広がるグリーンで、暖かな日射しの下、男に跨がり排泄する快感と開放感は、ほかでは決して味わえない。礼子は崇の顔の前に尻を出すと、中まで念入りに後始末させた。
次に、崇を馬にして、4番テーブルへと移動する。木製テーブルにセットされた座面が凹んだ丸太に頭を乗せるよう、崇に命じる。
崇の顔に座ると、レモンティを注文し、次第に激しくなるもがきの感触を心ゆくまで味わう。やがて、崇の意識は遠のき、礼子の巨尻の下でだらりと体を横たえるだけとなった。

Paradise's pleasures—the enjoyment and the feeling of liberation had while straddling a man and then excreting in him, all in the beautiful expanse of the green under the warm glow of the sun—these were pleasures not to be found elsewhere. Reiko pushed out her *oshiri* towards Takashi, who dutifully cleaned the remains.
Next, Reiko made Takashi serve as a horse to carry her to Table 4. She ordered Takashi to lay his head in the hollowed seat of a log chair that matched the wooden table next to it. Reiko sat on Takashi's face and ordered a lemon tea. His writhing beneath her became more and more intense and Reiko took her fill of this pleasurable sensation. But, soon enough, Takashi lost consciousness; his limp body stretched out passively beneath her massive buttocks.

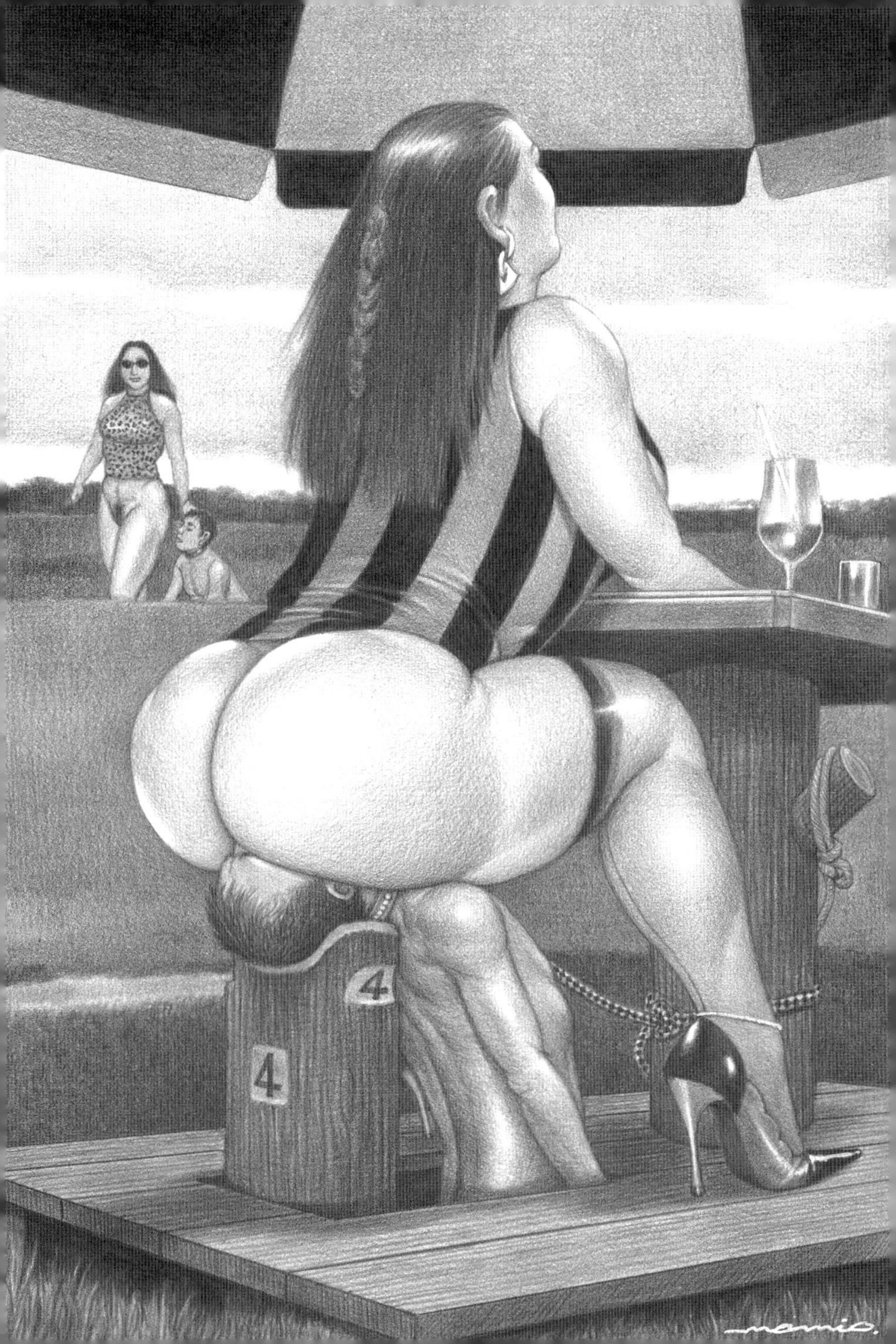
4
4

美しが丘高校バレー部に所属する、内村百合子と田原友子は、大の仲良しで、若さと好奇心から、いつでも一緒に遊びや買い物へと出かけた。2人とも180cmを超える身長と100kg近いグラマラスな体格を誇り、個性的な友子も正統派美人の百合子も学内の男子学生たちにとっては高嶺の花であった。カリスマ社長、大原加奈の後輩にあたり、2人は憧れの先輩が創り出した話題の楽園へさっそくやって来た。
百合子がはじめて人間椅子に座ってみる。
「とっても気持ちいいわ、女王様になった気分」
「でも百合子はお尻が特別大きいから椅子が可哀想よ」
「いいから友子もやってごらんよ。お尻から動きが伝わってきて気持ちいいわよ」
「そうね、男を虐めるために遊びに来たんだから、私も思い切り楽しむわ！　あれ、百合子、椅子が動かなくなっているよ」
「えっ、死んでないよね……?」

Uchimura Yuriko and Tahara Tomoko were both on the volleyball team at Beauty Hill High School; they were the greatest of friends. Sharing the curiosity of youth, the two were quick to travel or go shopping together. They both had glamorous figures, standing more than 180 cm tall and weighing over 100 kilos each. To the boys at school, the more conventional Tomoko and the more individualistic Yuriko were both prizes well beyond reach. Tomoko and Yuriko both were taken with the charismatic and famous graduate of their school, Ohara Kana, and they soon paid a visit to her famous Paradise. Yuriko first tried sitting in the human-chair.
"It feels so good. Like you're a Queen!"
"But Yuriko, your *oshiri* is so big, I feel sorry for the chair."
"It's nothing. Tomoko, you have to try it. You can feel the movement in your *oshiri* and it's very nice."
"Well, it is true that we came all the way here to abuse men. So, I won't hold back. But Yuriko, look, the chair's stopped moving."
"Oh, no. Is it dead?"    [180 cm = 5'11" / 100 kg = 220 lbs]

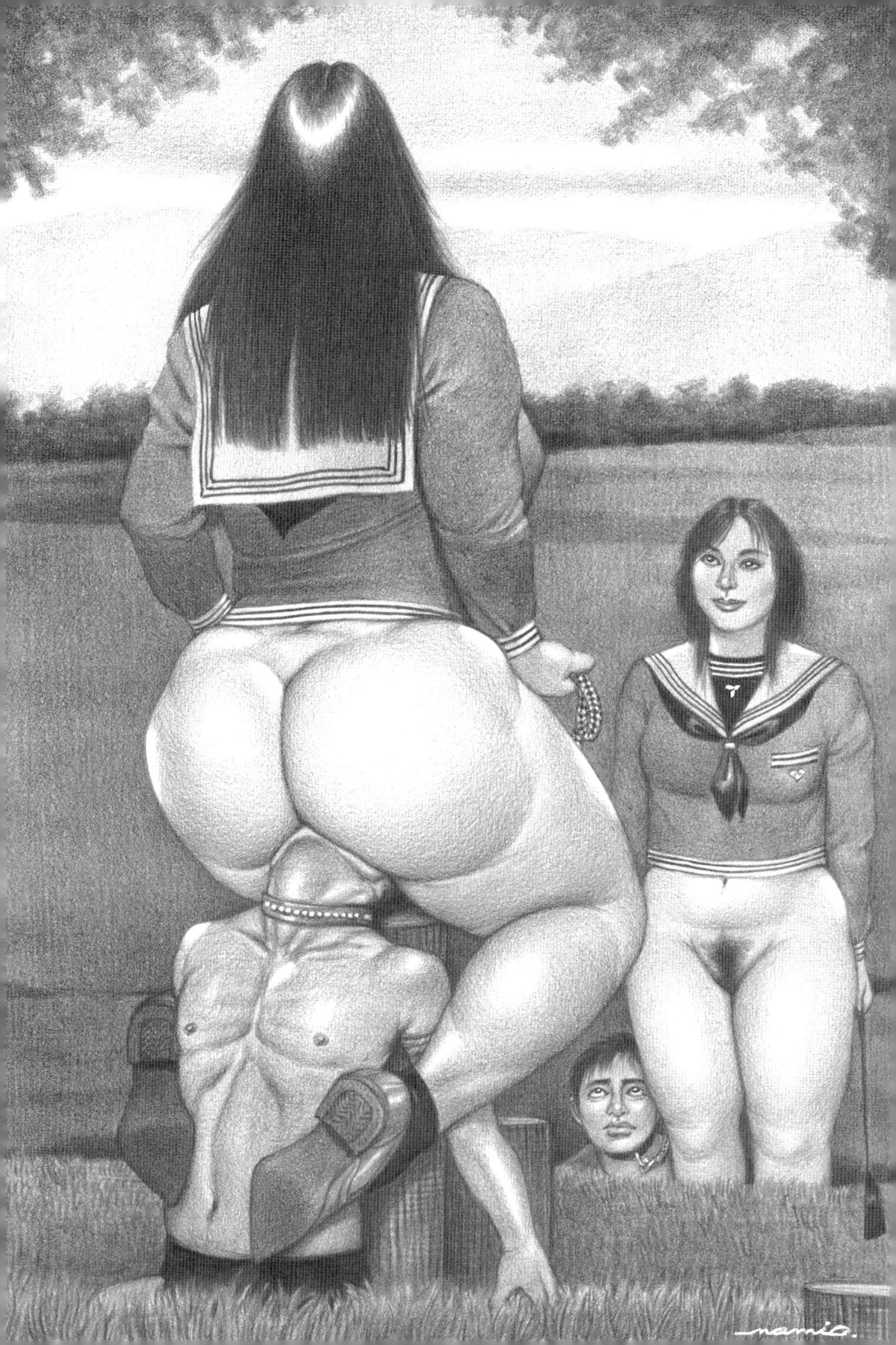
namio.

女子高生の百合子は開放的な野外で四つん這いになり無邪気に大股開きになり、男の前にお尻を出した。グイッと首輪の紐を引くと「舐めてごらん」と命じた。男は百合子のお尻のあまりの大きさに気圧された。
「何をびくびくしているの」
「お嬢様のお尻が神々しく畏れ多いのです」
「神々しいですって。嬉しいわ。それなら私をうんと楽しませてちょうだい」
百合子はお尻をさらに突き出し、ひもを引くと、男は一心不乱に舌を動かした。
「ああ、気持ちいい〜〈ヴヴヴ……〉はじめて口の中におならを出したわ。ウンチもしてあげたいけど、B級奴隷には無理なのよね、残念だわ!」

For a high school student like Yuriko, the liberating freedom of the outdoors encouraged her to get on all fours, guilelessly open her thighs, and stick out her *oshiri* in front of these men. She yanked on their leashes and ordered them to lick her. The men were overwhelmed by the extraordinary size of Yuriko's *oshiri*.
"What are you staring at?"
"Miss, your *oshiri* is so divine that I am humbled by it."
"You say it's divine. Well, that is very good to hear. If that's the case, then you'd better make me feel real good." Yuriko stuck out her *oshiri* even further, pulled the leash, and the man became completely absorbed in moving his tongue.
"Oh, that feels so good." She farted. "It's my first time to fart in a man's mouth. I actually want to feed him my shit, but he's only a Class B slave, so I mustn't. What a shame!"

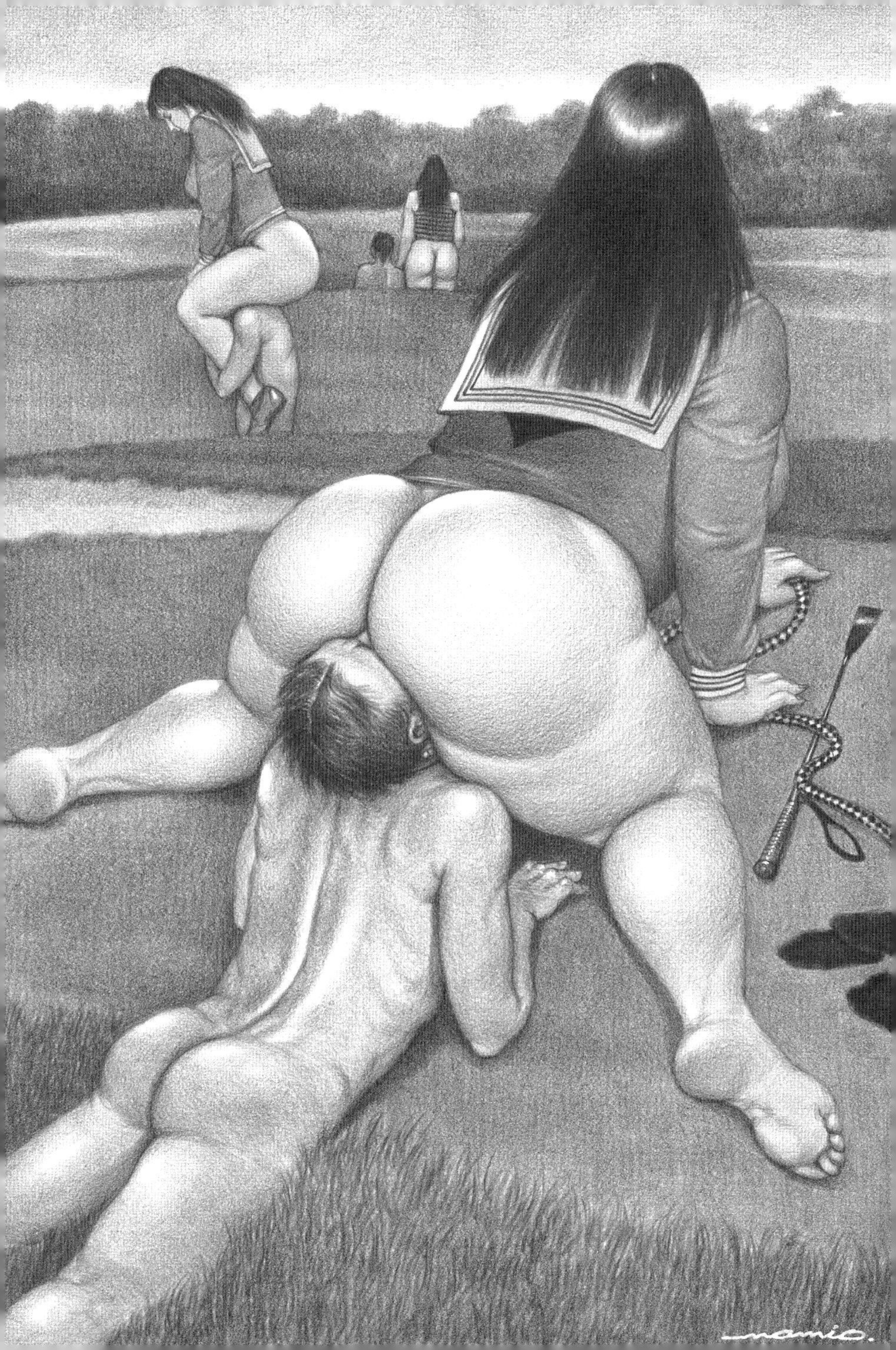
namio.

百合子を遠目に、友子も負けずに男に命じ、肩車でよろけながら木陰に移動した。そこで男を逆さにして足を木の幹に縛りつけると両手も根本に縛りつけ固定した。
「背もたれ付きの完璧な座椅子ができたわ」
こうして、男の顔に腰掛けると、大胆にもセーラー服を巻くりあげ、巨乳をさらした。
「こんな解放感ははじめて。お前には私のバストが見えないわね。でも、お前にはお尻の下がお似合いなのよ」
そう言うと、両足を持ち上げて体重をさらに掛けながら、舌奉仕を命じた。
男は友子に舌を飲まれたままやがて動かなくなった。

Not to be outdone by Yuriko, whom she could see in the distance, Tomoko was also ordering about her man. She moved haltingly on her man's shoulders into the shade. There, she turned her man upside down and secured him by tying his legs to the side of a tree trunk and his arms to its roots.
"Now I have a perfect legless ground chair, complete with its own back rest."
She lowered herself onto the man's face, and boldly lifted up her sailor suit to expose her massive breasts.
"I've never felt so free as this. You can see my bust, can you, boy? But, I think you fit much better down there, don't you?" Upon saying this, she lifted both her legs and, thus placing even more weight upon him, she ordered him to service her with his tongue. Before long, with his tongue caught inside Tomoko, the man ceased his movements.

nomio.

友子に刺激され、百合子の遊び心もエスカレートした。見渡すと、別の木に仕掛けがある。肩車で移動すると、それは人間ブランコ用のロープであった。さっそく、男の顔と胸が座面になるように、ロープに両手を繋ぎ、腰を下ろしてみた。両腕はちぎれそうに伸びきり、男は細かく震えているが、かまわずに、百合子はタバコをふかしながら、男の震えや痙攣を味わった。百合子が、ブランコを漕ぎ出すと、男の頭の中は真っ白になり、意識が遠のく。そして遠くから友子の声が聞こえてきた。
「ね〜、百合子、お腹空かない？　食事でもしようよ！」

Incited further by her friend, Yuriko's playfulness reached new levels. When she looked out, she could see a different apparatus on another tree. Using the shoulder saddle, she made her way over. Yuriko could see it was a rope meant for a human-swing. She attached her man by the arms so that his face and chest became the seat onto which she tried lowering herself. The trembling man's two arms were stretched almost to the ripping point, but Yuriko paid no attention and puffed at her cigarette all the while enjoying his quivering and his twitching. When Yuriko began to swing, the man's mind clouded as he came closer and closer to passing out. Just then, Tomoko could be heard calling in the distance. "Yuriko, are you hungry? Let's go eat!"

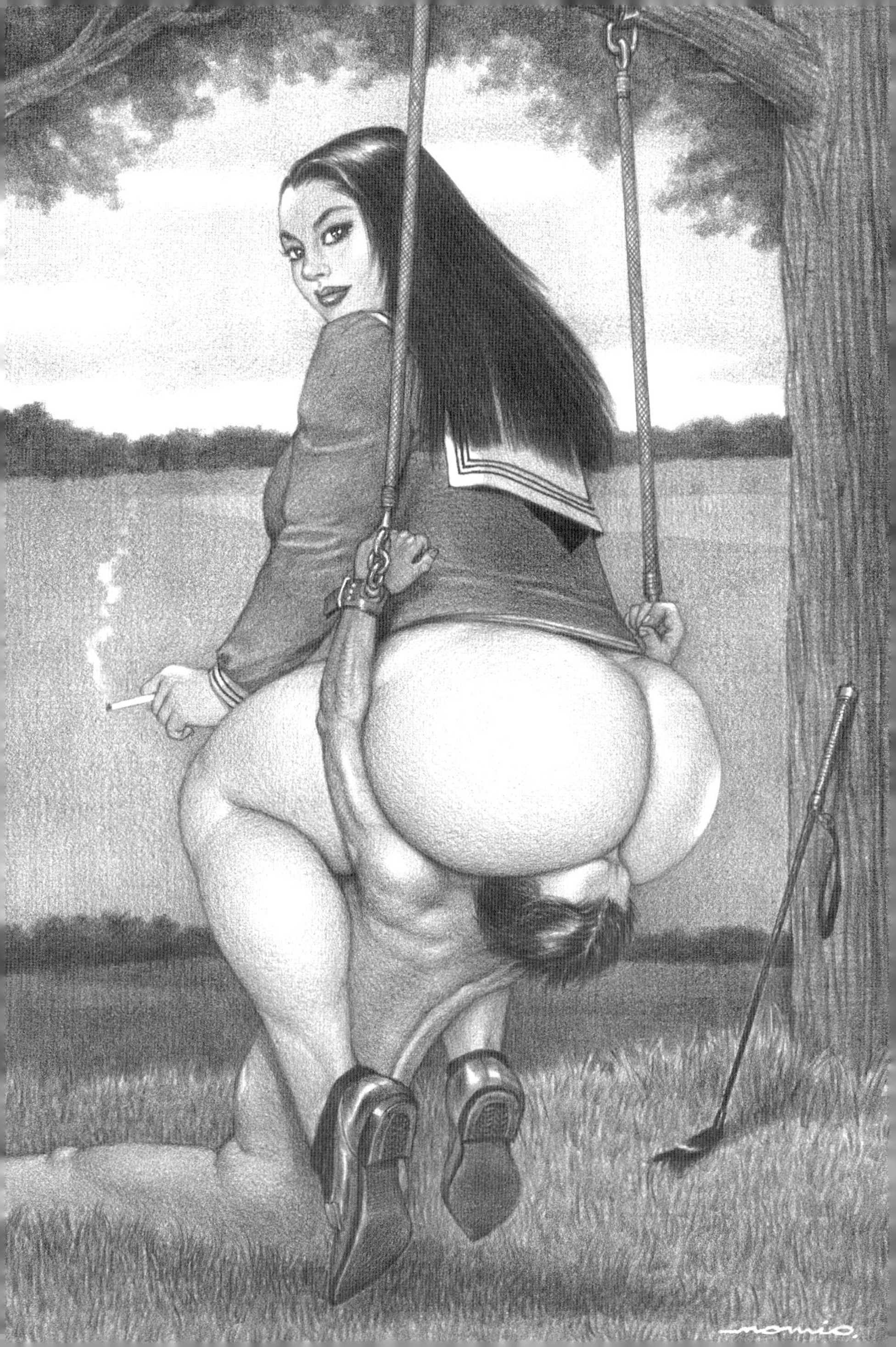
namio.

女性のパラダイス、"太陽の楽園"の噂は海外にも広まり、各国から来訪者を迎えた。

世界的なテニスプレイヤーでモデルとしても知られるロシアのマリア・シャラポナも楽園を訪れることになり、テニスコートが造られた。男たちも、天使のようなマリア様のお尻に敷いていただき、便器として使っていただけるかもしれないと、皆、色めきだった。

予想通り、マリアは東レパンパシフィックを制覇すると、翌日、楽園に現れ、美形の堂本健一と須田春樹を指名した。

テニスコートに案内され、感激したマリアは、さっそく持参した特性ベルトを装着してのプレイを希望した。腰にベルトを巻き、留め具に健一の両手を固定し、お尻に顔を挟んだまま一体となってプレイするのである。

「アア、イイワ。最高ノぷれいガデキソウ」

コートを走り回るマリアに、健一は全力でついて行った。

News of this women's utopia, Sun Paradise, soon spread overseas, and visitors came from every country. Following notice that the internationally-renowned Russian tennis player and model, Maria Sharapona, would be arriving, a tennis court was suitably constructed. All the men grew excited at the thought that they might be laid beneath the angelic Miss Maria and used as her toilet.

As expected, Maria won the Toray Pan Pacific. The day after her win, she descended upon Paradise where she requested as her personal slaves the stunningly handsome Domoto Ken'ichi and Suda Haruki.

Shown the new tennis court, Maria was duly impressed. She immediately donned the special belt that she'd brought with her and demanded to play. Maria wrapped this belt around her waist, and snapped Ken'ichi's hands into position. With his face firmly in her *oshiri*, the Mistress and her slave now moved as one being on the court.

"Ahh, ziss iss greattt. Verrry goot plaay." Maria ran about the court, and Ken'ichi followed with all his little might.

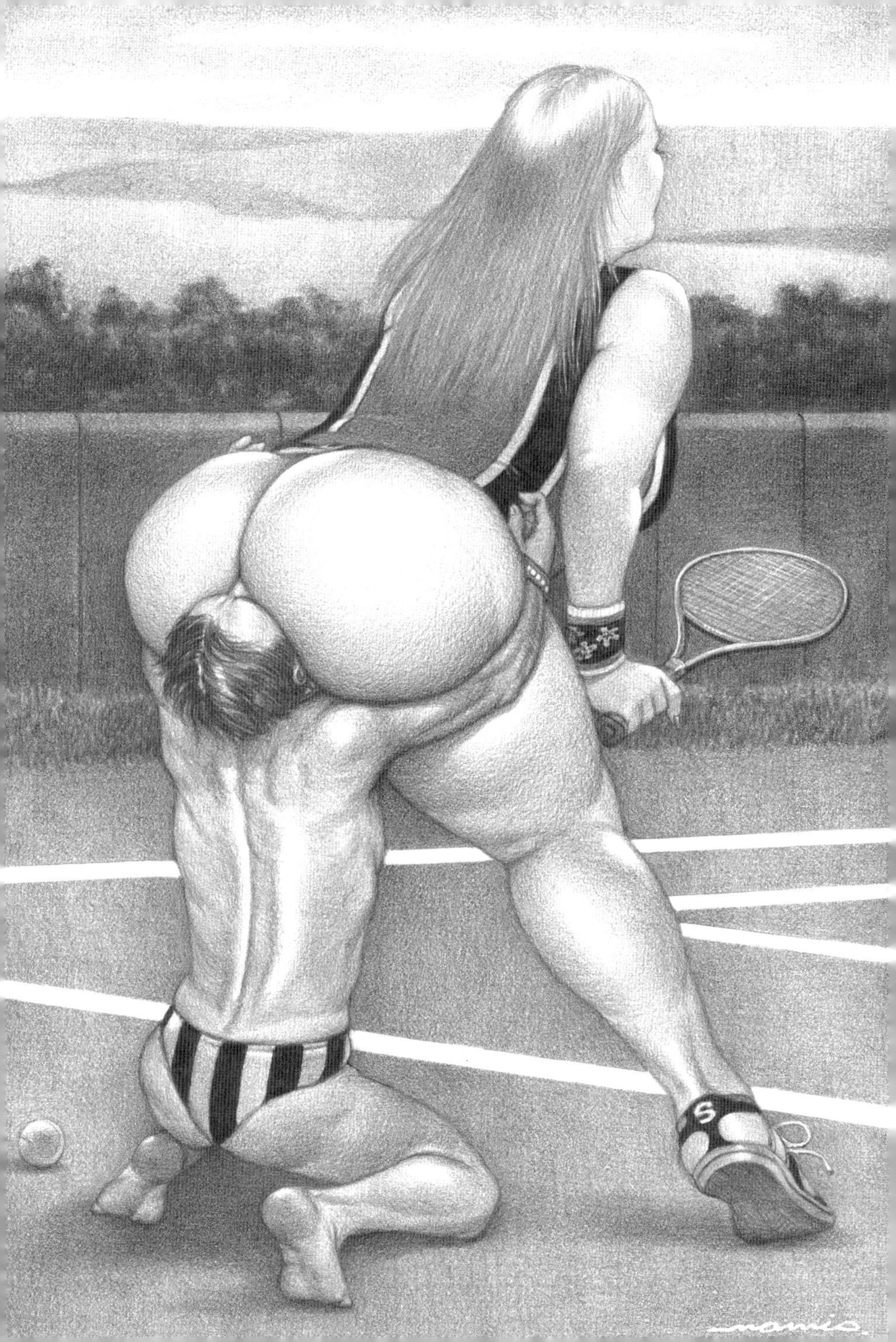

マリアの世界トップレベルのダイナミックな動きに健一の息はあがり足も追いつかず5分ももたずに失神した。春樹が交代したが、やはり、あっけなくダウンした。そこで、今度は2人を四つん這いの2頭立て馬車にして、その背に跨がり、グリーンへ移動した。そして健一を仰向けに寝かせると顔の上に座り休憩をとる。徐々に激しくなる健一のもがきを感じながら、「モットモット苦シメ!!」とますますのしかかる。動かなくなった健一の上で目映いお尻を誇示するマリアの目はサングラスの奥で笑っていた。

As a top-ranking world player, Maria moved quickly on the court, and the breathless Ken'ichi's legs couldn't keep up. Within five minutes, Ken'ichi had fainted. He was replaced by Haruki, but the latter too was down in a disappointingly short time. Maria next turned them into a two-man carriage and straddled their backs for them to lead her to the green. There, Maria rested upon the supine Ken'ichi's face. Enjoying Ken'ichi's thrashing about, which slowly became more and more violent, Maria pressed upon him, shouting, "Mohhr, mohhr! Yoouu sahhffer mohhr!" Above a finally motionless Ken'ichi, Maria showed off her dazzling *oshiri* and, behind her sunglasses, a twinkle could be detected in her eyes.

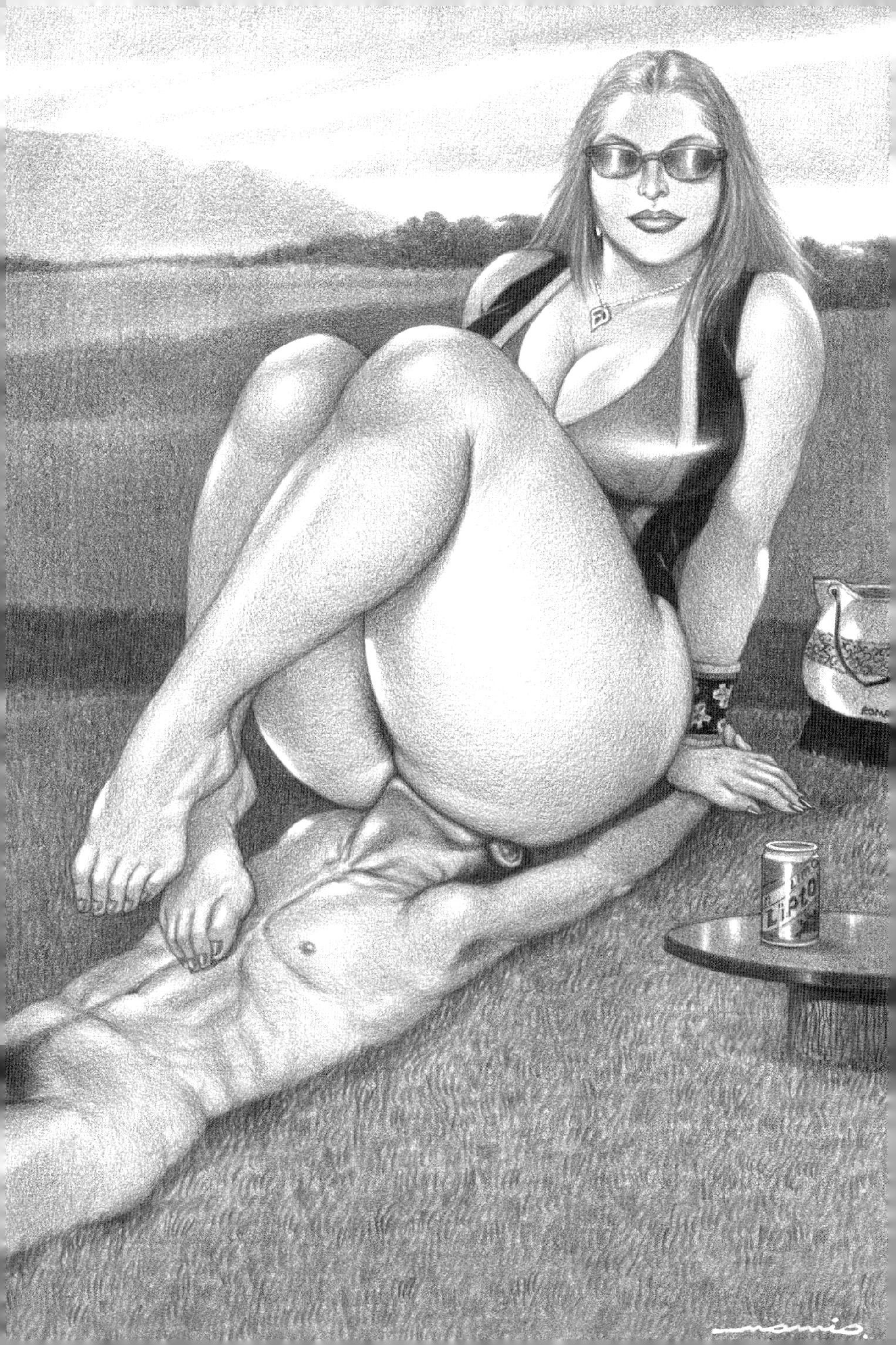

マリアのお尻の下で、失神した健一と春樹は、まるで夢を見ているのではないかというほど、幸福だった。そのままマリア様の美尻の下で殺されたいくらい、感激していた。

マリアが人間便器を希望したので、2人はまた馬車となり設置場所に向かった。マリアは春樹に便器を、健一に後始末を命じた。

穴に入り、便座に合わせた、ちょうどよい高さで待ち受ける春樹の目の前に、テニス界のスーパースター、マリア・シャラポナの見事なアヌスが息づき、放たれようとしている。

「サア、オ舐メ!!」

夢心地の春樹は懸命に舐めた。

「美味しいですマリア様、とても美味しいです」

「フフフ、モット美味シイモノヲアゲルワ!」

マリアの体内の一部が、空気にも触れず、何物も介さずに春樹の体へと吸収された。神聖な授受の光景である。

Unconscious beneath Maria's *oshiri*, Ken'ichi and Haruki were both so happy; it was as if they'd both died and entered Paradise. They were both so overwhelmed they wished they could die right there beneath Maria's beautiful buttocks.

Maria requested use of a human-toilet, so the two became her carriage again to escort her to one of the established facilities. Maria requested Haruki for her toilet and Ken'ichi for clean-up. Haruki entered the hole, specially designed to position his head right at the seat level, and waited. And from that vantage point, he could see the splendid anus of the tennis superstar Maria Sharapona, a living, breathing anus that seemed ready to explode.

"Haaarry uppp. Liiick."

As if in a rapture, Haruki began to lick desperately.

"It is so delicious, Mistress Maria. So very delicious."

"Hah, hah! I giiive yoouu somezing mohhhr deeleeeshass."

Without once being exposed to the outside air, a part of Maria's body devolved directly into Haruki's own. This was the scene of a Holy Passage.

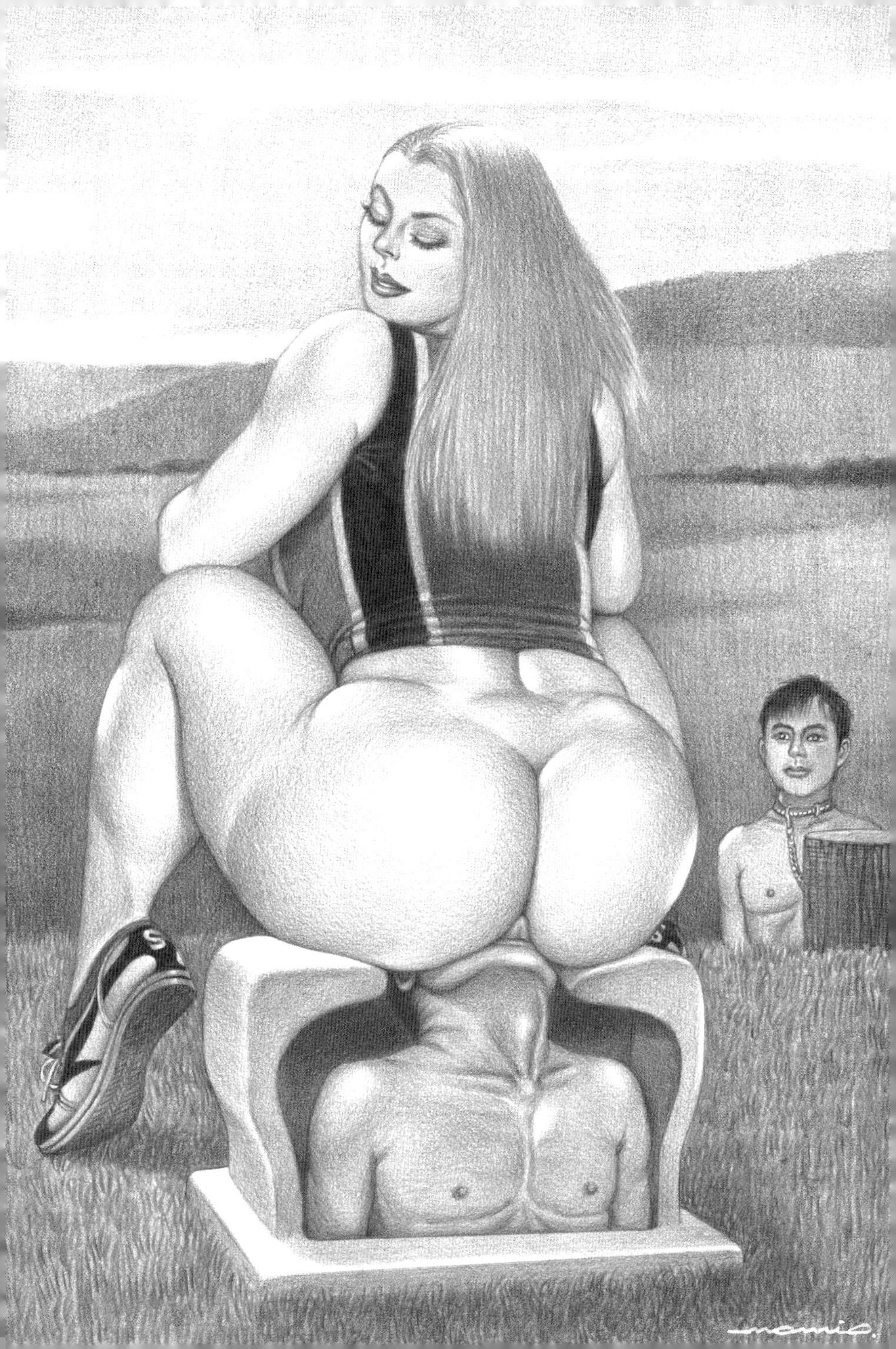

自分の命令には絶対服従する、小さく健気な日本の男たち。こんな可愛い男が欲しい、連れて帰りたいというマリアの強い要望で、春樹を専属奴隷として連れて帰ることが許された。

帰国前夜、マリアは楽園の客室で特製椅子に座り、食事を楽しんでいた。豊満なヒップの下から春樹の顔がわずかに見える。17才とはいえ、鍛えあげ、世界を制した肉体は女王の風格をたたえ、その巨尻に埋もれ舌奉仕をする春樹は人間以下の存在に映る。それでも春樹の頬には歓喜の涙が伝わっていた。

食事を終えるとマリアは、そのまま春樹に口を開かせ、食事を与え、お尻を揺らして笑った。果たして、春樹はマリアの巨尻の下でいつまで生き延びることができるのだろうか。

These small and admirable Japanese men, who would swear to faithfully follow her every command—Maria truly adored them! In fact, she strongly hoped she might be able to take one of these charming men with her when she left. It was decided that Maria could bring Haruki home as her personal slave.

The evening before her departure, Maria enjoyed her dinner from the comfort of one of the special chairs provided in Paradise's guest quarters. A bit of Haruki's head could be made out from under her large hips. Although a young seventeen, Maria's well-trained body had dominated the world. It brimmed with the style of a queen. Buried in those tremendous buttocks, Haruki was offering tongue service. To some, he may have appeared less than human, but such appearance notwithstanding, Haruki's cheeks were stained with tears of joy.

After dinner, Maria had Haruki open his mouth, gave him his dinner, shook her *oshiri*, and laughed. How long could it last? How long might Haruki prosper under Maria's ample buttocks?

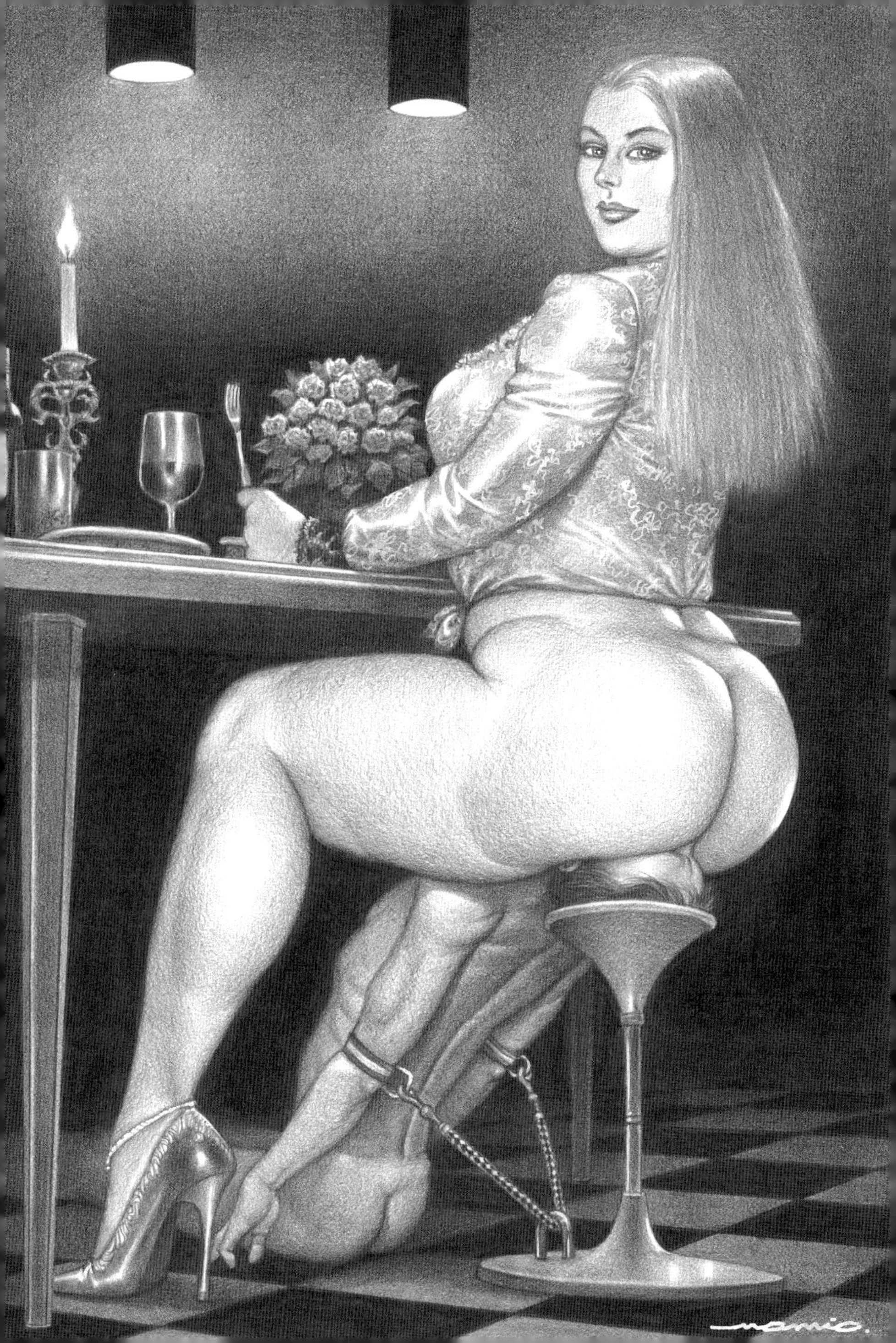
namio.

大原加奈は重厚なソファに腰掛け、両足を大きく広げ、ワインを楽しみながら、男の奉仕に酔っていた。ソファの下には奴隷用のピットがあり、両手を拘束された男が上半身を出し、クレバスに顔を埋め、舌を動かしている。加奈にゴルフ場と全財産を献上した石田信男である。
「信男も舌の使い方が上達したわね。今日はとてもよく感じるわ。そうよね、これが信男の最後のご奉仕だものね。心がこもっているわ。存分に奉仕なさい」
信男にとって加奈は女神であり、最大の望みは女神に命までも捧げることである。それゆえに巨尻の下で「死ぬ」のでなく、「殺されたい」のである。
「信男、もっともっと気持ちよくさせなさい。さ、たっぷり飲ませてあげるわ、いくわよ」
信男は涙を流しながらノドを鳴らした。

Ohara Kana sat down in a stately armchair, opened her two legs wide, and began to enjoy both wine and the service of a man. At the foot of the sofa, there was a sunken cubicle hollowed out of the floor from which a slave could service. With both arms tied, his torso was visible above the floor. His face buried in her crevice, he was moving his tongue back and forth. This was Ishida Nobuo, the man who had given Kana his golf course and his estate.
"Nobuo, your tonguing skills have improved. Today, they feel very good. That's right—I'd forgotten. Today is your last service. That's why your heart is into it. Well, you can do it as much as you like."
For Nobuo, Kana was his Goddess. And his greatest wish was to offer his life to this Goddess. That's why he didn't want to simply die beneath the tremendous buttocks, rather he wanted to be killed by them.
"Nobuo, I want it to feel much, much better. I've got a big drink for you now. Go on, drink up!"
Nobuo shed tears as his throat gurgled the urine.

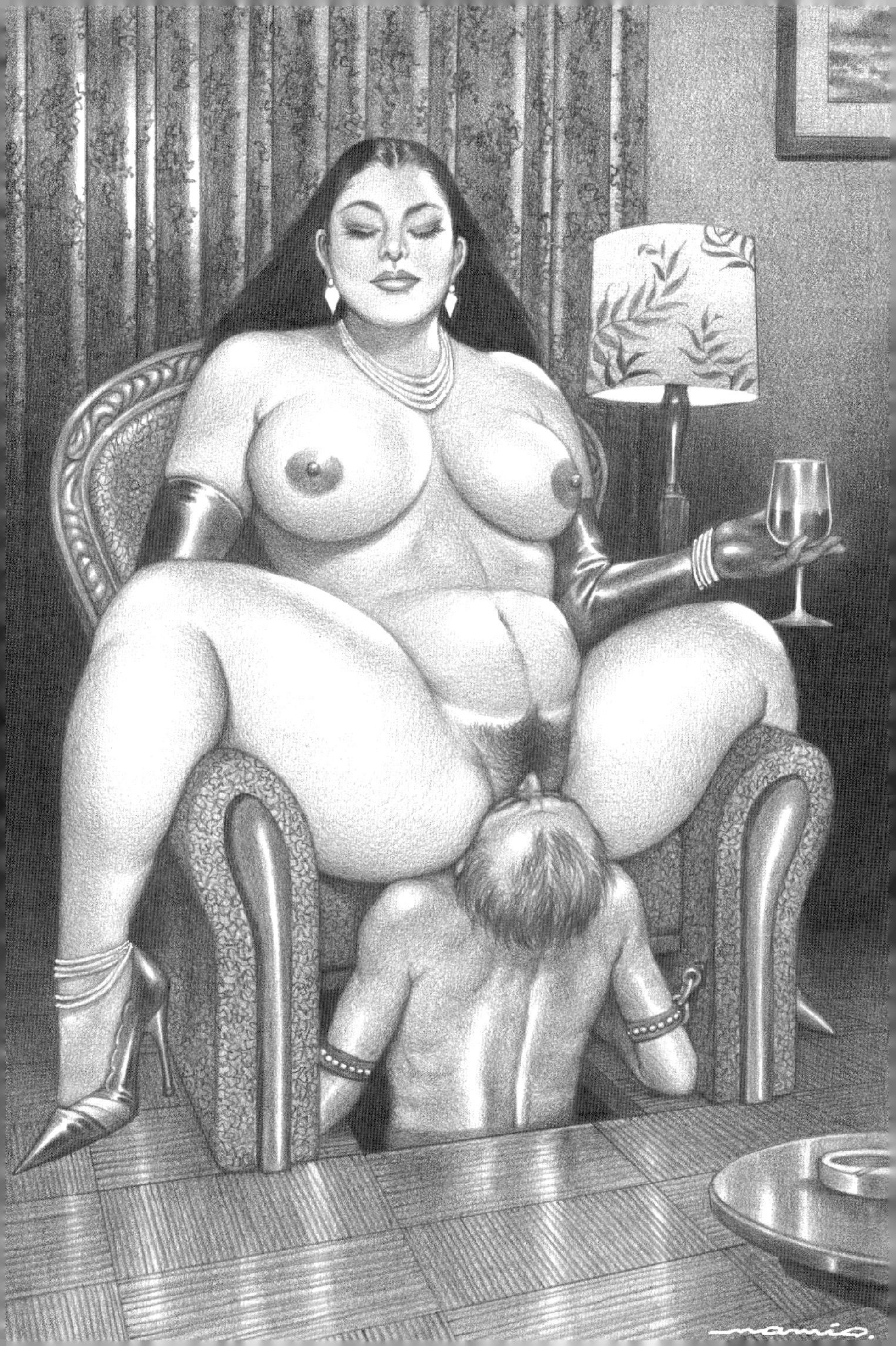

「信男、来なさい、早く!」
加奈の号令でピットから飛び出すと、慌てて後を追い、仁王立ちになった加奈の後ろに正座をして、輝くお尻を仰ぎながら、次の命令を待つ。
加奈は微笑みながら、豊かに盛り上がったお尻を信男の前に出し、舐めるように命じた。
口を近づけ舌を伸ばす信男のために、加奈が腰を割る。
剛毛を掻き分け舌を動かすと、その舌を押し返すように、お尻の穴が盛り上がり、開かれる。信男は再び頬を涙で濡らしながら、夢中ですべてを収めた。
「お前は最高の便器よ」
「ありがとうございました。加奈様、私は幸せ者です」

"Nobuo, come quick!" At Kana's order, Nobuo jumped from the cubicle. Hurriedly he followed Kana. He sat on his knees behind the towering Kana. Staring up at the shining *oshiri*, he awaited her next words.
Smiling all along, Kana stuck her generously plump *oshiri* in front of Nobuo and ordered him to lick. So that Nobuo, his tongue extended and his face nearing, could better lick her, Kana bent lower and spread her legs. Nobuo parted the pubic growth with his tongue. As if it were pushing back against the outstretched tongue, the *oshiri* hole perked up and opened. Tears once again streaming down his face, an enraptured Nobuo took it all in.
"You are the best toilet."
"Thank you very much, Mistress Kana. I am the happiest man."

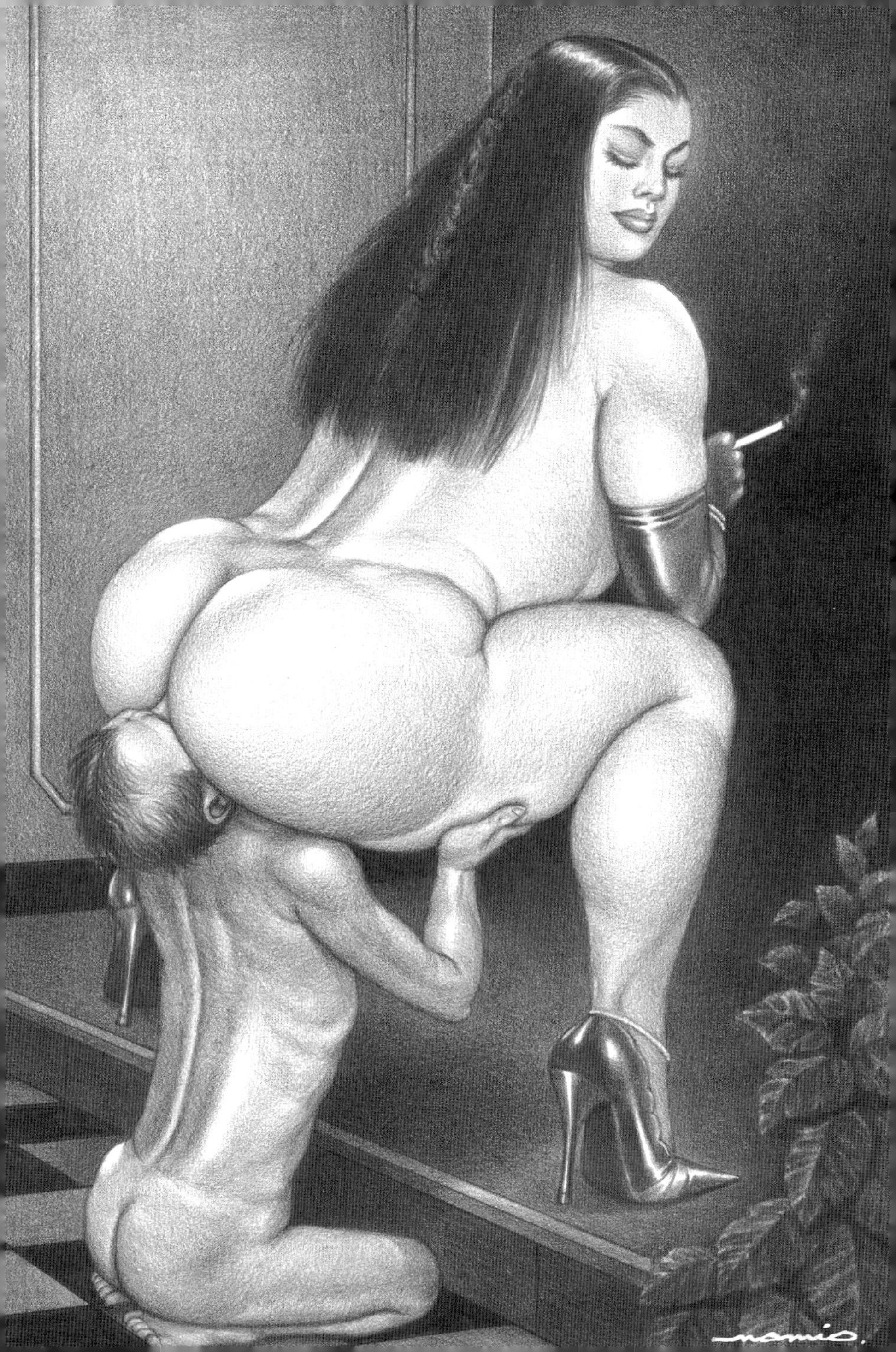
namio.

「いよいよ、望みを叶えてあげるわ。来なさい」
これまで、お尻の下で失神させた男は数知れないが、息の根を止めるのは初めてである。そのままお尻の下で殺してしまいたいと何度も思ったが、それが実現するのである。きっと最高のエクスタシーが得られるに違いない。
薄暗い部屋にはローソクの光が揺れ、中央に十字の形をした処刑用の椅子が置かれている。
「加奈様、最高に幸せです。私を殺してください!」
加奈は信男に命じ、座面に頭を置かせると、両手両足を縛り椅子に固定した。そしてタバコに火をつけ、ゆっくり信男の顔を跨ぐ。
「石田信男の死刑を実施する!」
恐怖におののき目を見張る信男の顔に、巨大なお尻が下ろされ、股の上に足が置かれた。
「信男、死ね。私の巨尻の下で死ね」
加奈のサディズムが頂点に達し、昇りつめたとき、細かく震えていた信男の動きは止まった。

"Now, I will finally grant your wish. Come here."
Although she had made a countless number of men faint, this was the first time for Kana to take a breathing soul. She had thought many times how she might like to kill a man as he lay beneath her *oshiri*, but now she was to make this fantasy real. Surely this must be the ultimate ecstasy.
Candlelight glimmered in the darkly lit room, and in the center there was a an execution chair in the shape of a crucifix. "Mistress Kana! This is the greatest pleasure. Please kill me!"
Kana ordered Nobuo to place his head upon the chair. She tied both arms and both legs, and secured him to the chair. Upon lighting a cigarette, she slowly straddled Nobuo's face. "I now sentence Ishida Nobuo to death."
Trembling in terror and opening wide his eyes, Nobuo saw the massive buttocks descending upon him and could feel the foot upon his crotch.
"Die, Nobuo! Die beneath my tremendous ass…"
Kana's sadism was reaching its zenith, and when it had finally found that apex, Nobuo's delicate tremors had stopped.

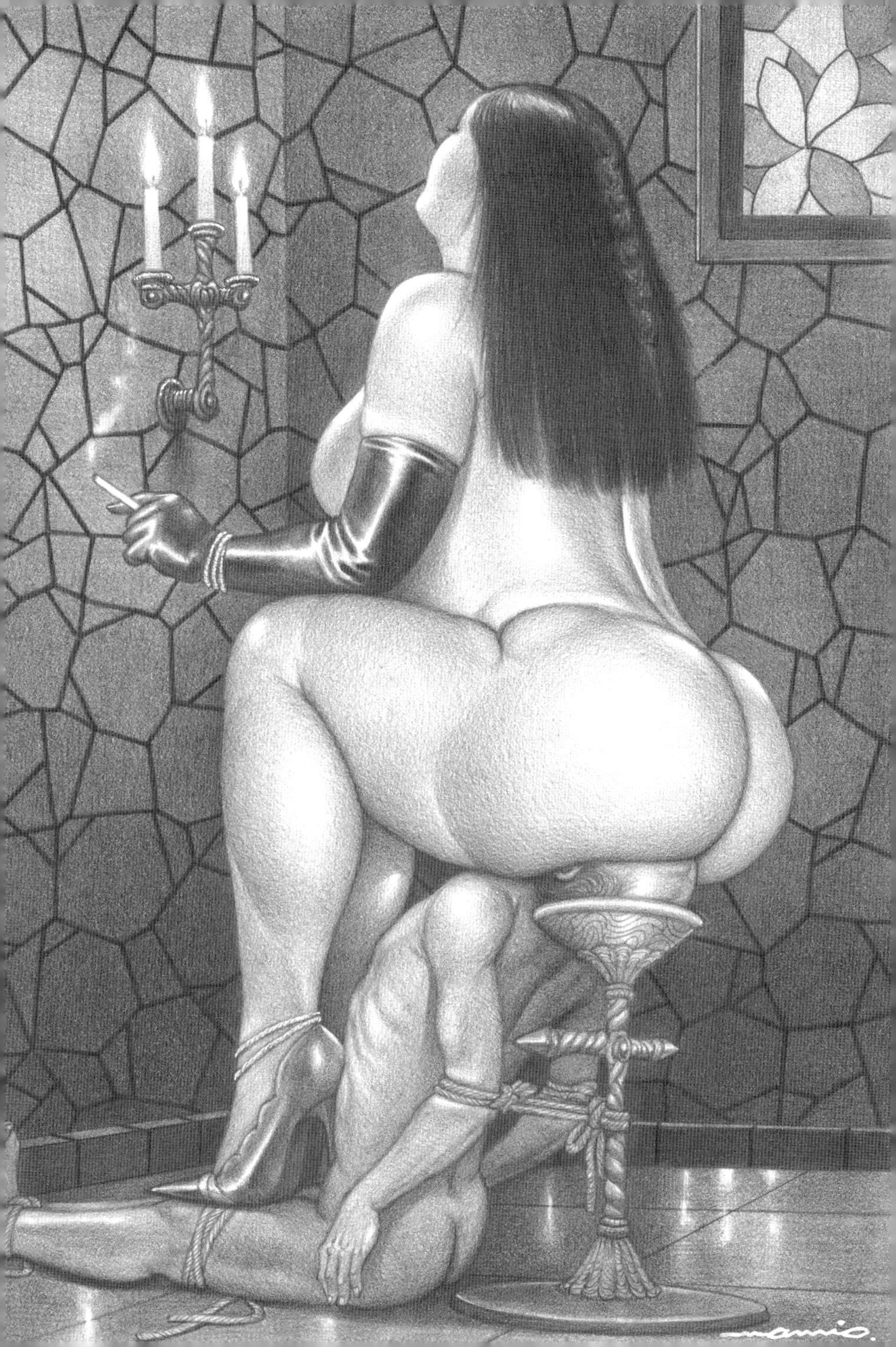

お尻の下で冷たくなっていった信男の感触が快感とともに今も甦る。ベッドに横たわり、律子に舌奉仕させる加奈が感覚を反芻する。
「私は本当にサディストなのね。あれほど感じるとは思わなかったわ。律子の首もこのまま締めてしまおうかしら、フフ。安心なさい。あなたは舌も柔らかくて上手だから、殺さず、奴隷にしておいてあげる」
扉の向こうの声が、謁見希望の男の到着を伝える。全裸で入場するように命じると、平伏す男を睨み、加奈は尋ねた。
「それで、私に献上する瀬戸内海の無人島は広いの?」
「はい、周囲10kmでございます」
「ちょうどいいわ。第二の楽園が出来るわね。よし、お前は当分、私の便器として使うわ。それで、望みは何なの? 言ってごらん」
「加奈様の偉大なお尻に敷いて頂きたいです」
「ほほう、死ぬかもしれなくてよ、お前はその覚悟ができているのね……オホッホッホホホ……」

Along with the pleasure, Kana could later still summon the sensation of Nobuo's cold body beneath her *oshiri*. Sprawled across the bed, Kana recalled the experience while Ritsuko was providing the tongue service she'd ordered.
"I really am a sadist. I never thought it would feel so good. Ritsuko, should I strangle you just the same way? Ha, ha! Don't worry. Your tongue is so soft and skillful, I'd never kill you, just make you my slave."
Noises from the other side of the door meant the man hoping for an audience with Kana had arrived. She ordered him naked into the room. Glaring at the prostrate man, she demanded:
"The desert island you've promised me, the one in the Inland Sea—tell me how large it is."
"Ten kilometers in circumference, Mistress."
"Just the right size. I will build my second Garden of Paradise. And you, for the time being, I'll be using you as my toilet. So what do you want? Go ahead and spit it out!"
"I would like Mistress Kana to lay me beneath her tremendous *oshiri*."
"Heh, heh, heh. You might just die there. You've come prepared for that, I take it. Ha! Ha! Ha! Ha!" Kana's laugh trailed off...

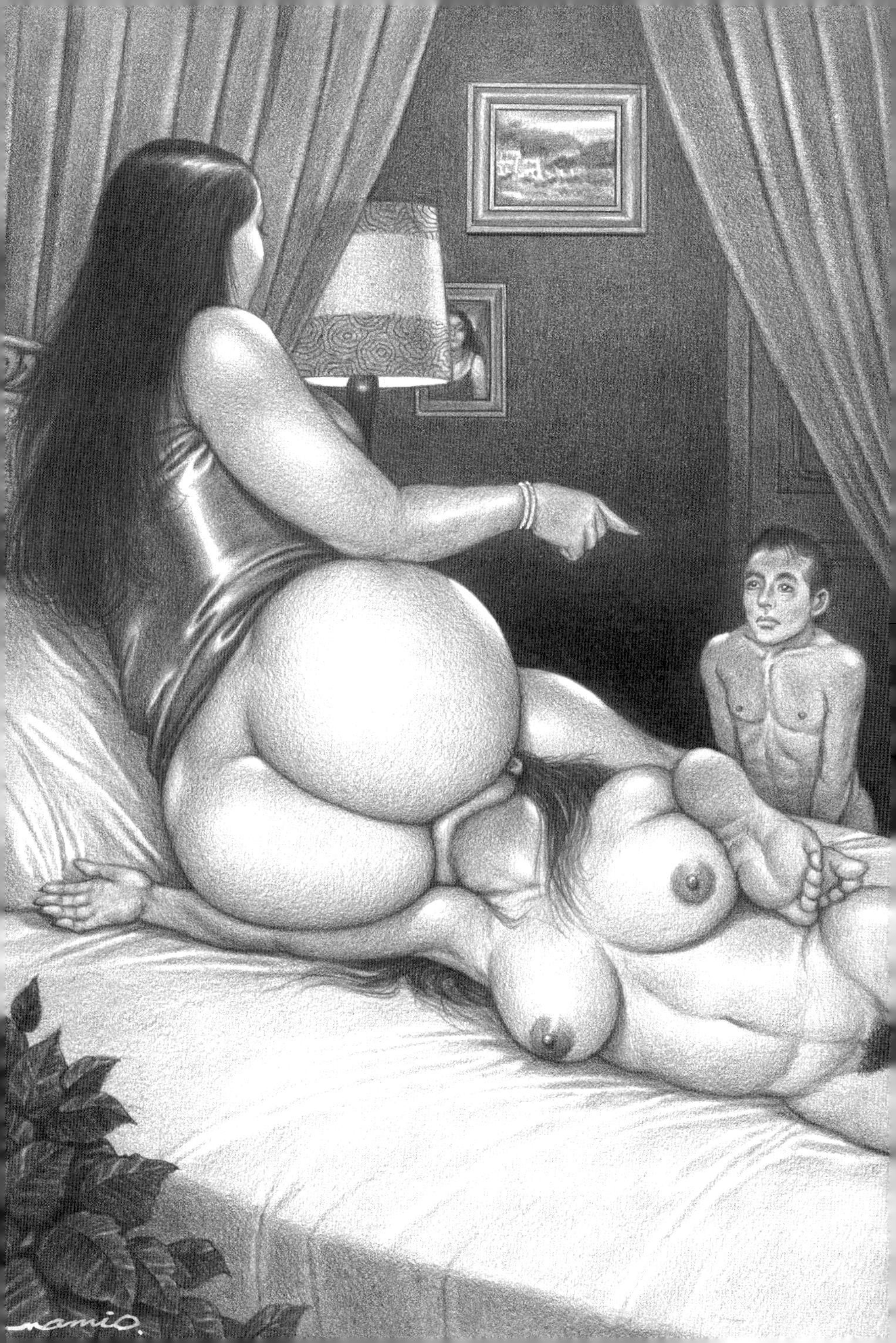
namio.

Fin

# Profile

春川ナミオ

1947年大阪生まれ。筆名は女優・春川ますみと谷崎潤一郎の『痴人の愛』のヒロイン・ナオミに由来する。高校時代より、カストリ雑誌の草分け「奇譚クラブ」の読者投稿欄に、作品を寄稿。美しく豊満で気高い女性と、彼女に奉仕する男をモチーフに一貫して男性マゾヒズムを描き、この分野の第一人者の地位を確立する。画業の他にも関連AVのパッケージイラストを手がけ、アドバイザーなども務める。

HARUKAWA Namio
Born 1947 in Osaka, Japan. Harukawa's distinctive penname combines the name of film actress Harukawa Masumi with an anagram of Naomi, the heroine in Tanizaki Jun'ichiro's novel *Chijin no ai* [A Fool's Love]. While in high school, Harukawa began contributing work to the readers' column of *Kitan Club*, postwar Japan's leading pulp magazine. Since then, Harukawa's drawings of male masochism have portrayed noble, voluptuously beautiful women and the men who would serve them. Harukawa is now recognized as the preeminent Japanese illustrator specializing in the depiction of women's ass. In addition to his drawings on paper, Harukawa has also created cover artwork for numerous SM porn video productions and has served as a consulting editor for several other projects derived from his work.

(Tanizaki's tale of masochism is published in English under the title *Naomi*. Harukawa Masumi stars in Shohei Imamura's *Intentions of Murder* and also appears in the same director's classic *The Insect Woman*.)

[著作一覧]
- ……SMコレクター8月号増刊『痴人の愛』(K.K.サン出版、1980年)
- ……『処刑島の女王』(夢屋、1996年)
- ……『巨女渇愛　気貴き大女と畜獣の痴的恋愛物語　春川ナミオ妖美画集』(マイウェイ出版、2000年)
- ……『巨女渇愛VOL. 2　巨女の魅力に酔い痴れて』(マイウェイ出版、2002年)
- ……『聖女の臀堂』(TACO ché、2002年)
- ……『CALLIPYGE』(United Dead Artists 仏、2008年)

Other Works by Harukawa Namio:
*Chijin no ai* [A Fool's Love], supplemental August 1980 number of *SM Korekutâ* (SM Collector), Tokyo: K. K. San shuppan, 1980.
*Shokeitô no joô* [Queen of Execution Island], Tokyo: Yumeya shuppan, 1996.
*Kyojo katsuai: Kedaki ôonna to chikujû no chiteki ren'ai monogatari—Harukawa Namio yôbi gashû* [Parching Love for Giant Women: A Tale of Foolish Love Between Lofty, Large Ladies and Their Domesticated Slaves—A Collection of Harukawa Namio's Seductive Beauty], Tokyo: Maiwei shuppan 2000.
*Kyojo katsuai Vol. 2: Kyojo no miryoku ni yoishirete* [Parching Love for Giant Women II: Mesmerized by the Allure of Giant Women], Tokyo: Maiwei shuppan, 2002.
*Seijo no dendô* [Cheeky Temple to Holy Women], Tokyo: TACO ché, 2006.
*Callipyge*, Archères, Yvelines: United Dead Artists, 2008.

Note to the English Reader: The Japanese word *oshiri* (pronounced o-shee-ree) is no special word. Nor is the *oshiri*, as Harukawa's pictures and stories reveal, in any way the special preserve of the Japanese populace. Many a foreigner can sport a fine *oshiri*—and most on our planet carry at least a serviceable one. Still, for a tale from a culture where contemporary clothing presents the *oshiri* much more than conceals and where the *oshiri* is almost always a pleasant thing, the rhyming vowels of *shiri*—prefixed appropriately by the polite, even honorific, *o*—has seemed the best way to convey the humor, the charm, and the wonder of this magnificent thing.

This translation preserves, in all instances, the Japanese order of family, then given name. To encourage an effortless, pleasurable read, it does not employ macrons for long Japanese vowels, except in the list of author's works. The translator would like to thank Nasu Yukari, Nakayama Ayumi, and Kitajima Yuji for their vital suggestions for this work of translation. All errors are those of the translator. No offense is intended in the representation of dialect or accent, meant to parallel foreign accents in the Japanese original.

**Translation by: Dominic Wolfe**

編集●中山亜弓　デザイン●小久保由美

発行●2012年7月27日［第一版第一刷］　2024年9月25日［第一版第五刷］

発行所●ポット出版

150-0001 東京都渋谷区神宮前2-33-18 #303　電話 03-3478-1774　ファックス 03-3402-5558
ウェブサイト http://www.pot.co.jp/　電子メールアドレス books@pot.co.jp
郵便振替口座　00110-7-21168　ポット出版

印刷・製本●シナノ印刷株式会社

ISBN978-4-7808-0183-5 C0071　©HARUKAWA Namio

絵物語
# ドミナの園

春川ナミオ

ドミニク・ウルフ　英訳

AN ILLUSTRATED STORY
# GARDEN OF DOMINA
HARUKAWA NAMIO
TRANSLATED BY DOMINIC WOLFE

EDITOR: NAKAYAMA AYUMI　DESIGNER: KOKUBO YUMI
FIRST PUBLISHED IN TOKYO JAPAN, JUL. 25, 2012
BY
POT PUB. CO., LTD.
#303 2-33-18 Jingumae Shibuya-ku Tokyo, 150-0001 JAPAN
E-Mail: books@pot.co.jp　http://www.pot.co.jp/
Postal transfer: 00110-7-21168

ISBN978-4-7808-0183-5　C0071　©HARUKAWA Namio, 2012

書籍DB●刊行情報

| | | | | | |
|---|---|---|---|---|---|
| 1 データ区分 | 1 | 13 著者名1 | 春川　ナミオ | 24 判型 | A5 |
| 2 ISBN | 978-4-7808-0183-5 | 14 種類1 | 著 | 25 ページ数 | 168 |
| 3 分類コード | 0071 | 15 著者名1読み | ハルカワ　ナミオ | 27 本体価格 | 2800 |
| 4 書名 | 絵物語　ドミナの園 | 22 出版年月 | 201207 | 33 出版者 | ポット出版 |
| 5 書名ヨミ | エモノガタリドミナノソノ | 23 書店発売日 | 20120727 | 39 取引コード | 3795 |

本文……コスモエアライト・ナチュラル・A判・Y目・55.0kg（141μm）／スミ
表紙……レザック66・鼠・四六判・Y目・260kg／スリーエイトブラック
カバー・帯……オーロラコート・菊判・T・93.5kg／スリーエイトブラック／ラミネートタック・PETグロス／箔押し［KATANI／30］
使用書体……游明朝体　游ゴシック体　本明朝　Bodoni Copperplate Fling Univers
2024-0105-1.0（5.0）